The Writer's Craft

Spelling and Vocabulary Booklet

Green Level
Grade 8

McDougal Littell Inc.

A Houghton Mifflin Company

Evanston, Illinois   Boston Dallas Phoenix

To the Teacher

The Spelling and Vocabulary Booklet consists of two parts: Spelling Masters and Vocabulary Lessons. A description of each element follows.

Spelling Masters

The ten Spelling Masters for this grade are designed to strengthen students' understanding of key spelling conventions. The lessons can be used for whole-class or small-group instruction or for independent study.

The lesson on each Spelling Master consists of a word list and a spelling generalization followed by three exercises. The word lists are made up of words that students frequently misspell. These words were identified through extensive error analysis of student writing and standardized tests. The first exercise is designed to provide students with practice in writing words from the list. In the second exercise, students are asked to apply the spelling generalization from the lesson to new words. The last exercise makes the connection between spelling and writing by having students proofread writing for errors in grammar, usage, capitalization, and punctuation, in addition to spelling errors related to the generalization presented in the lesson.

Vocabulary Lessons

The vocabulary section is designed to strengthen and expand students' vocabularies and to prepare them to take the Scholastic Assessment Tests. This vocabulary series is based on lists of words frequently found on standardized tests such as the SAT and the ACT. The exercises are similar to the ones students will encounter when they take such tests. There are three booklets, one each for Grades 6–8. Each booklet is composed of 36 vocabulary lessons, and each lesson contains 20 vocabulary words. The parts of speech and definitions of the words are given, along with sample sentences and two sets of exercises.

The words for the vocabulary lessons have been classified by grade level and organized into categories. The use of categories allows students to associate each word with others that are similar in meaning, form, or function. The definitions and the sample sentences correspond to the category in order to provide a context for learning each word. Although many of the words have multiple meanings and forms, the most common definition and part of speech that are appropriate to the category are given for each word.

Each lesson includes a sentence completion exercise followed by a synonym exercise, an antonym exercise, or an analogy exercise. Each word is used at least once in the exercises.

You may wish to introduce the words at the beginning of the week and allow students to complete the exercises as independent study. At the end of the week, you may want to test the students' mastery of the words by asking them to write the words, define them, and use them correctly in original sentences.

ISBN 0-8123-8848-8

5 6 7 8 9 10 – MDO – 99 98

CONTENTS

Strategies for Teaching Spelling

Research has shown that most students go through several predictable stages of development in learning to spell (Henderson and Beers 1980; Gentry 1984; Henderson 1985; Templeton 1986, 1991; Nelson 1989). These stages may be identified as follows:

1. During the phonetic **letter-name stage,** students conceptualize words in a left-to-right, letter-by-letter fashion. The name of the letter is a primary criterion that students use for spelling a word.
2. In the transitional **written-word-pattern stage,** students begin to use more complex letter sequences in place of the one-letter/one-sound strategy.
3. At the **syllables and affixes stage,** students begin to learn what happens at the juncture where prefixes and suffixes are joined to single-syllable words to form two-syllable words.
4. In the final stage, the **derived forms stage,** students learn more complex word information based on meanings, such as related word forms, root words, and words derived from other languages.

Students in grades 6–8 most commonly function within the third and fourth stages of spelling development. For example, students at stage three are likely to make spelling errors in words that require doubling a final consonant or dropping a final *e* before adding a suffix that begins with a vowel: droping *(dropping),* makeing *(making).* At stage four, students' errors tend to reflect their continuing attention to sound rather than the meaning characteristics of words: *musision (musician).* The Spelling Masters address the most common kinds of errors made by students at these stages. They can be adapted to a prescriptive approach or presented as traditional spelling lessons.

Prescriptive Approach

Using this approach, the teacher regularly analyzes the errors in a student's writing, making notes about the type and frequency of errors. Writing samples from all subject areas should be examined. When a pattern of errors emerges, that is, when a student consistently misspells words containing a particular letter pattern, the teacher points out the problem to the student and presents the lesson that addresses that spelling generalization. If the teacher discovers that several students or the entire class are making the same type of error, any lesson may also be used for small-group or whole-class instruction. Note that, using a prescriptive approach, the lessons may be presented out of order, and some lessons may not be used at all.

Traditional Approach

Using a traditional approach, the Spelling Masters would be presented to the class in the order they appear in this book. To teach the lesson, the teacher might present the word list and spelling generalization on Monday and have the class work through the exercises independently. Later in the week, the exercises would be corrected orally.

No matter which approach you choose , you might wish to suggest that students use one or more of the following strategies to improve their spelling:

1. Encourage students to keep a personal spelling journal in which they list in alphabetical order the troublesome words or words they wish to learn. Suggest that students highlight or underline elements of the word that they find especially tricky or difficult to remember.
2. When students are learning to spell new words, encourage them to use an approach that engages a variety of senses. Such an approach might involve visual study of the word, oral practice, mental imaging, and written practice. For example these procedures could be followed:

   Look at the word.
   Say the word.
   Spell the word.
   Copy the word.
   Picture the word.
   Cover the word and write it.
3. Suggest that students create mnemonic devices and other memory aids to help them remember the lesson pattern. One such aid might be the phrase "the amazing disappearing *e.*"

References

Gentry, J. Richard. "Developmental Aspects of Learning to Spell." *Academic Therapy* 20 (Sept. 1984): 11-19.

Henderson, Edmund H. *Teaching Spelling.* Boston: Houghton Mifflin, 1985.

Henderson, Edmund H., and James W. Beers, eds. *Developmental and Cognitive Aspects of Learning to Spell: A Reflection of Word Knowledge.* Newark, Del.: International Reading Association, 1980.

Nelson, Laurie. "Something Borrowed, Something New: Teaching Implications of Developmental Spelling Research." *Reading Psychology* 10.2-3 (1989)

Templeton, Shane. "Synthesis of Research on the Learning and Teaching of Spelling." *Educational Leadership* 43 (Mar. 1986): 73-78.

———. "Teaching and Learning the English Spelling System: Reconceptualizing Method and Purpose." *The Elementary School Journal* 92.2 (Nov. 1991)

Final silent e words and suffixes

festive	festiv<u>ity</u>	festiv<u>ely</u>
severe	sever<u>ity</u>	sever<u>ely</u>
time	tim<u>ing</u>	tim<u>ely</u>
love	lov<u>ing</u>	lov<u>ely</u>
defense	defens<u>ive</u>	defens<u>eless</u>
age	ag<u>ing</u>	ag<u>eless</u>
confine	confin<u>ing</u>	confin<u>ement</u>
endorse	endors<u>ing</u>	endors<u>ement</u>
amuse	amus<u>ing</u>	amus<u>ement</u>
achieve	achiev<u>ing</u>	achiev<u>ement</u>

A **suffix** is a word ending that changes the use of a word.

When you add a suffix that begins with a vowel to a word that ends with a silent *e*, drop the final *e*. Keep the *e* if the suffix begins with a consonant.

Exceptions: true—truly   argue—argument   awe—awful
whole—wholly   nine—ninth

Practice the Words
Choose one of the spelling words above to fill the first blank in each pair of blanks below. Then use a different form of that word to fill the second blank.

1. _____ your goal will not be easy, but any great _____ in life requires hard work and discipline.

2. In the Middle Ages, nobles often punished criminals by _____ them to a dungeon. The _____ sometimes lasted for years.

3. The criminal received a _____ sentence due to the _____ of his crime.

4. The bank requires an _____ on every check. _____ a check is easy; just sign your name on the back of it.

5. Flowers and other decorations gave the room a _____ look appropriate for the _____ that was planned for that evening.

6. Ponce de León hoped to solve the problem of _____ by finding the Fountain of Youth and remaining forever _____.

7. Mom suggested that we _____ ourselves by watching television, but we found it much more _____ to watch our cat play with its new toy.

8. The lioness jumped instantly to the _____ of her _____ newborn cubs.

9. Romeo fell instantly in _____ with the _____ Juliet.

10. In sports, _____ refers to physical and mental coordination, not the

measurement of _____ itself.

Apply What You Know
To each base word add suffixes to form two new words. Possible suffixes are listed below. Write the new words on the lines.

-ly	-ing	-or	-ed	-able	-ure
-er	-ion	-ive	-less	-ment	-ial

1. like   _____   _____

2. complete   _____   _____

3. intense   _____   _____

4. price   _____   _____

5. state   _____   _____

6. finance   _____   _____

7. legislate   _____   _____

8. engage   _____   _____

Proofreading Practice
Proofread the following consumer advice column. Use proofreading marks to correct the mistakes in grammar, capitalization, punctuation, and spelling.

To avoid purchaseing items you will latter regret owning, follow these

rules. first, never buy impulsivly. Second, research more expenseive items

to see if they meet you're requirments and to see if they can be bought for

a more lower price. Don't be impressed by celebrities' endorsements of

products. Taking time to be a carful consumer will save you time money,

and aggravation in the end.

Spelling Master 2
Final y words and suffixes

convey	conveys	conveyed	conveying
display	displays	displayed	displaying
employ	employs	employed	employing
subway	subways		
attorney	attorneys		

apply	applies	applied	applying
defy	defies	defied	defying
envy	envies	envied	envying
celebrity	celebrities		
century	centuries		

If the letter before a final **y** is a vowel, do not change the **y** when you add a suffix.

Exceptions: day + *-ly* = daily

If the letter before the final **y** is a consonant, change the **y** to **i** before you add any suffix except *-ing*. The **y** never changes before *-ing*.

Exceptions: dry + *-ness* = dryness   shy + *-ness* = shyness

---

Practice the Words

Complete each sentence with a word from the list. Write the word on the line.

1. By boycotting British goods, American colonists _____ the Stamp Act.

2. _____ from the entertainment world are often invited to the White House to perform for visiting foreign dignitaries.

3. In the president's absence, the vice president _____ greetings and good wishes to the prime minister.

4. In 1976 the United States marked two _____ of democratic government with many bicentennial celebrations.

5. Several million people are _____ by the executive branch of the federal government.

6. The Judiciary Act of 1789 established the U.S. Supreme Court and allowed for _____ to aid the party filing a suit.

7. Each justice on the Supreme Court _____ his or her own legal views and judgment in deciding cases.

8. Fireworks _____ and the _____ of the American flag are often part of Fourth of July celebrations.

9. As American cities grew in the late nineteenth century, mass-transit innovations such as cable cars, trolley cars, and _____ were introduced.

10. During the California gold rush, bitter disputes sometimes broke out because one prospector _____ the claim of another prospector.

Apply What You Know

Add the suffixes *-s, -es, -ed,* or *-ing* to the base words below to form words that match the definitions. Write each new word beside the appropriate definition.

medley	tally	controversy	modify
justify	dignify	theory	decoy

1. explanations or hypotheses _____

2. making slight changes in something _____

3. supplied good grounds for; warranted _____

4. musical arrangements made up of parts from many musical pieces _____

5. arguments or differences _____

6. entered or counted _____

7. showing stateliness or formality _____

8. things used to lure _____

Proofreading Practice

Proofread this excerpt from a letter to the editor. Mark the mistakes in grammar, capitalization, punctuation, and spelling.

There are a number of controversys over the plan to build a network of

subwayes connecting two suburban Countys to the City. The most

important issue is whether such a costly project is justifyed. Some

independant transportation agencys have suggested a modifyed version of

the plan that seems more realistically. The Commission needs to examine

all it's alternatives before undertaking such an enormous project.

Spelling Master 3

Adding suffixes

fit	fitting	fitted	fitness
mad	madder	maddest	madly
sum	summed	summary	sums
zip	zipped	zipper	
blur	blurred	blurring	

sweet	sweetest	sweetener	sweetly
weak	weaker	weaken	weakness
steal	stealing	stealer	steals
dark	darker	darken	darkness

> A word that has **1** syllable, **1** vowel, and **1** final consonant is called a
> **1 + 1 + 1** word. To add a suffix beginning with a vowel to a **1 + 1 + 1** word,
> first double the final consonant: fit—fitted. Do not double the final consonant
> when adding a suffix that begins with a consonant.
>
> For one-syllable words that are not **1 + 1 + 1** words, do not double the
> final consonant.

Practice the Words

The words in each group are related in some way. Find and write a spelling word that
fits into each group.

1. dimmed, smeared, fuzzied   _____

2. snap, button, hook   _____

3. added, figured, totaled   _____

4. appropriateness, applicability, suitability   _____

5. charmingly, agreeably, pleasantly   _____

6. lessen, soften, decrease   _____

7. thieving, robbing, looting   _____

8. synopsis, outline, recap   _____

9. wildly, rashly, crazily   _____

10. deepen, blacken, shade   _____

11. amounts, values, totals   _____

12. fault, failing, flaw   _____

Apply What You Know

Circle the **1 + 1 + 1** words below. Then use the clues to determine which suffixes need to be added to the base words to complete the puzzle. All the words will be used. Use a dictionary if you need help.

wood   beg   fun   rain   throb   heir   thin   shear   stun   eat

Across
3. Dazed or astounded
6. A female heir
7. The most humorous
8. A person who asks for money
9. Pouring down
10. Pulsating

Down
1. Consumed
2. Made of wood
4. Opposite of thickest
5. Removing by cutting or clipping

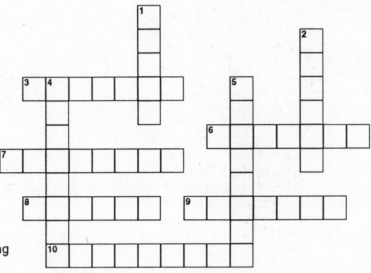

Proofreading Practice

Proofread the following fairy tale. Mark the mistakes in grammar, capitalization, punctuation, and spelling.

There once was a Pauper who fell maddly in love with a woman whom happened to be the heirress to a large fortune. Each night he spoke to her under the cover of darkness. The woman was charmed by this mysterious visitor and ask him to marry her. At this, the young man disclosed that he was poor. Althouugh stuned by his revelation, the woman said "I would rather marry a begar than a bragart any day" Thus, the two were married and lived happy ever after.

Spelling Master 4
More about adding suffixes

permit	permitted	permitting
admit	admitted	admittance
occur	occurring	occurrence
submit	submitted	submitting

| infer | inferring | inference |
| prefer | preferring | preference |

benefit	benefited	benefiting
edit	edited	editor
travel	traveled	traveler
credit	credited	crediting

Before adding a suffix beginning with a vowel to a word of two or more syllables, double the final consonant only if both of the following conditions exist:

1. The word ends with a single consonant preceded by a single vowel.
2. The word is accented on the last syllable: ad mit'.

Note: If the newly formed word is accented on a different syllable, the final consonant is not doubled: in fer' in' fer ence

---

Practice the Words

An analogy is a special way of showing how words are related to one another. Complete each analogy with a spelling word so that the second pair of words has the same relationship as the first pair of words.

1. **Survey** is to **surveyor** as **edit** is to _____.

2. **Committing** is to **committed** as **submitting** is to _____.

3. **Persevere** is to **perseverance** as **admit** is to _____.

4. **Rescue** is to **rescuer** as **travel** is to _____.

5. **Deter** is to **deterrence** as **occur** is to _____.

6. **Farmer** is to **farming** as **creditor** is to _____.

7. **Defeat** is to **defeated** as **benefit** is to _____.

8. **Refer** is to **reference** as **infer** is to _____.

9. **Exist** is to **existed** as **permit** is to _____.

10. **Confer** is to **conference** as **prefer** is to _____.

Apply What You Know

Mark the accented syllable in each base word below. Then use the clues to write the related forms of the words on the spaces provided. Use a dictionary to check your answers.

o mit	con cur	pro fit	re cur	can cel
quar rel	of fer	in cur	re mit	com mit

1. crossing out; withdrawing (v.) __ __ __ __ __ __ __ n g

2. failed to include; left out (v.) __ __ __ __ __ __ d

3. bringing upon oneself (v.) __ __ c __ __ __ __ __ __

4. the sending of money (n.) __ __ __ __ __ __ __ n c __

5. argued (v.) __ __ __ __ __ __ __ __ d

6. the act of happening again (n.) __ e __ __ __ __ __ __ __ e

7. happening at the same time (adj.) __ __ __ __ __ __ __ e n t

8. did something bad or wrong (v.) c __ __ __ __ __ __ __ __

9. gift or donation (n.) __ __ __ __ __ __ __ g

10. reaped an advantage; benefited (v.) __ __ __ __ __ __ __ d

Proofreading Practice

Proofread the following movie review. Mark the mistakes in grammar, capitalization, punctuation, and spelling.

If you like exciting movies, then I highly recommend "<u>An Occurence at</u>

<u>Owl Cave</u>." The movie is about Adam, a time traveller who is transported

to a prehistoric age. He is permitted to join a primitive clan of cave people

and it is soon evident to he and the audience that he will be submited to a

number of trials. Somehow adam endures a grate deal of sufferring.

Although the story is admitedly a little far-fetched, the acting is very

beleiveable. If you enjoy Science Fiction, then you wo'nt be disappointed

by this action-packed adventure.

Spelling Master 5
Adding prefixes

re- + strain	=	restrain	*re-* + cess + *-ion*	=	recession
pro- + claim	=	proclaim	*pro-* + cess + *-ion*	=	procession
con- + genial	=	congenial	*con-* + cess + *-ion*	=	concession
in- + corporate	=	incorporate	*per-* + suade	=	persuade
dis- + satisfied	=	dissatified	*dis-* + suade	=	dissuade

A **base word** is a complete word to which other word parts can be added.

A **root** is a word part that cannot stand alone. It must be joined to other word parts to form a word.

Prefix		Root		Suffix		Word
+		+		=		
re-		cess		*-ion*		recession

A **prefix** is a group of letters added to the beginning of a base word or root to change its meaning. When a prefix is added to a base word or root, the spelling of the base word or root remains the same.

Practice the Words

Write the spelling word that best describes each situation. Each word can be used only once.

1. _____ Mom's decision to give in to our pleading and allow us to stay up late came as a surprise.

2. _____ Use every argument you can think of to convince Molly to join us.

3. _____ The chairman will publicly announce the winner as soon as all the votes are tallied.

4. _____ Professor Uchida tried to discourage the student from dropping out of college.

5. _____ The officer had to hold the offender down so he would not struggle or try to escape.

6. _____ Stephen was unhappy with the quality of the equipment.

7. _____ We formed lines and marched up to the platform to receive our diplomas.

8. _____ There was a temporary downturn in business activity.

9. _____ The committee is going to rewrite its report in order to include Tom's suggestions.

10. _____ Erica and Carmen have the same tastes and temperament and get along very well.

Apply What You Know

Follow the code to add prefixes and suffixes to the roots in these pyramids.

The root **dict** means "to speak."   The root **ject** means "to throw."

1. $\underset{5}{\underline{\ \ }}$ dict

2. $\underset{14\ \ 5\ \ 12}{\underline{\ \ }\ \underline{\ \ }\ \underline{\ \ }}$ dict

3.   dict $\underset{1\ \ 13\ \ 5\ \ 4}{\underline{\ \ }\ \underline{\ \ }\ \underline{\ \ }\ \underline{\ \ }}$

4.   dict $\underset{1\ \ 13\ \ 10\ \ 12}{\underline{\ \ }\ \underline{\ \ }\ \underline{\ \ }\ \underline{\ \ }}$

5. $\underset{11\ \ 12\ \ 5}{\underline{\ \ }\ \underline{\ \ }\ \underline{\ \ }}$ dict $\underset{7\ \ 10\ \ 9}{\underline{\ \ }\ \underline{\ \ }\ \underline{\ \ }}$

6. $\underset{3\ \ 10\ \ 9\ \ 13\ \ 12\ \ 1}{\underline{\ \ }\ \underline{\ \ }\ \underline{\ \ }\ \underline{\ \ }\ \underline{\ \ }\ \underline{\ \ }}$ dict $\underset{10\ \ 12\ \ 15}{\underline{\ \ }\ \underline{\ \ }\ \underline{\ \ }}$

7. $\underset{12\ \ 5}{\underline{\ \ }\ \underline{\ \ }}$ ject $\underset{5\ \ 4}{\underline{\ \ }\ \underline{\ \ }}$

8. $\underset{4\ \ 5}{\underline{\ \ }\ \underline{\ \ }}$ ject $\underset{7\ \ 10\ \ 9}{\underline{\ \ }\ \underline{\ \ }\ \underline{\ \ }}$

9. $\underset{10\ \ 2}{\underline{\ \ }\ \underline{\ \ }}$ ject $\underset{7\ \ 9\ \ 6}{\underline{\ \ }\ \underline{\ \ }\ \underline{\ \ }}$

10. $\underset{11\ \ 12\ \ 10}{\underline{\ \ }\ \underline{\ \ }\ \underline{\ \ }}$ ject $\underset{7\ \ 10\ \ 9}{\underline{\ \ }\ \underline{\ \ }\ \underline{\ \ }}$

11. $\underset{11\ \ 12\ \ 10}{\underline{\ \ }\ \underline{\ \ }\ \underline{\ \ }}$ ject $\underset{7\ \ 8\ \ 5}{\underline{\ \ }\ \underline{\ \ }\ \underline{\ \ }}$

12. $\underset{7\ \ 9\ \ 13\ \ 5\ \ 12}{\underline{\ \ }\ \underline{\ \ }\ \underline{\ \ }\ \underline{\ \ }\ \underline{\ \ }}$ ject $\underset{5\ \ 5}{\underline{\ \ }\ \underline{\ \ }}$

A	B	C	D	E	G	I	L	N	O	P	R	T	V	Y
1	2	3	4	5	6	7	8	9	10	11	12	13	14	15

Proofreading Practice

Proofread these directions on how to take good photographs. Mark the mistakes in grammar, capitalization, punctuation, and spelling.

Nobody should feel inhibitted by using a camera. By following some

basic guidelines you can become an acceptional Photographer. For

instance, watch the way the light reflect off your subject or you will get

undesirable shadows. Also, pervent objects, such as you're finger from

obstructing the lens. Third, try to judge the distance between you and your

subject carefully. Or your photograph will be fuzzy. Most importantly keep

presevering. With practice you may eventually take exhibittion-quality

photographs.

Spelling Master 6
Indistinct vowels and related word forms

popular	popularity	ordinary	ordinarily
regular	regularity	temporary	temporarily
familiar	familiarity	imaginary	imagination
author	authority	history	historical
major	majority	victory	victorious

Unstressed **a** or **o** before the letter **r** may be difficult to identify. To remember the correct spelling of words containing **-ar/-or** and **-ary/-ory**, first think of related forms in which the vowel is stressed. Then use other clues to help you distinguish these unstressed vowels. Here are some examples.

- The ending **-ar** often follows the letter **l**.
- The ordinary **-ary** is more common than **-ory** and **-ery**.
- The ending **-or** often refers to a person or an occupation. Both **-or** and **-ory** frequently follow the letter **t**.
- An unstressed vowel sound in the middle of a three-syllable word is often dropped when the word is pronounced: *his to ry* becomes *his try*. Do not forget the unstressed syllable when you spell these words.

Practice the Words
Find a spelling word to complete each sentence. Then write the word as though it had to be divided between the two lines of the sentence. Check your answers in a dictionary. Remember to add a hyphen after the break.

1. Mr. Benedict is an _____

   _____ on American history.

2. The Union army was _____

   _____ at Gettysburg.

3. We are studying the _____

   _____ of civilization on earth.

4. Do you prefer _____

   _____ coffee or decaffeinated?

5. The equator is an _____

   _____ line that circles the earth.

6. What determines the _____

   _____ of a movie?

7. Are you _____

   _____ with the language?

8. We _____

   _____ attend church on Sunday.

9. The phone is _____

   _____ out of service.

10. Whoever gets the _____

    _____ of votes will win.

Apply What You Know

Add the missing letter and mark the accented syllable in each word below. Then follow the instructions to change each word to a related form. Write the new word in syllables and mark the accent. Use your dictionary.

1. pe cu li__r   Add *-ity.*   _____

2. mem __ ry   Change the *y* to *i;* add *-al.*   _____

3. mi n__r   Add *-ity.*   _____

4. ed i t__r   Add *-ial.*   _____

5. so l__r   Add *-ium.*   _____

6. reg u l__r   Add *-ity.*   _____

7. sec re t__r y   Add *-ial.*   _____

8. vol un t__r y   Change the *y* to *i;* add *-ly.* _____

9. su pe ri __r   Add *-ity.*   _____

10. li br__r y   Change the *y* to *i;* add *an.*   _____

Proofreading Practice

Proofread this article from a brochure for new students. Mark the mistakes in grammar, capitalization, punctuation, and spelling.

How do you cope with entering a new school? Here is some tips. to

make new friends, seek out students with interests that are simelar to

your's instead of trying to join the populor crowd. One way to do this is to

join after-school clubs and activities. Keeping your grades up can be a

majer problem. so do your homework regulerly. Ask your teachers for help

if you need it. To avoid getting lost, familiorize you with the building before

school starts. Create clever memmory tricks to help you remeber your

locker combination. Do'nt worry. You'll be a pro in no time at all.

Spelling Master 7
Silent letters

desi<u>gn</u>er	conde<u>mn</u>
dou<u>bt</u>ful	ca<u>lm</u>ly
<u>ps</u>ychology	nu<u>mb</u>ed
spa<u>gh</u>etti	<u>rh</u>ythmic

A few consonants are silent in certain letter combinations:

<u>gn</u>   <u>bt</u>   <u>ps</u>   <u>gh</u>   <u>mn</u>   <u>lm</u>   <u>mb</u>   <u>rh</u>

Practice the Words

Circle the word in each phrase that is similar in meaning to a spelling word. Write the spelling word. Expand each phrase into a sentence in which the word you circled is replaced with the spelling word.

1. uncertain about _____

_____

2. peacefully reassured _____

_____

3. enjoyed the beat _____

_____

4. cooked the noodles and sauce _____

_____

5. the fashion artist _____

_____

6. deadened by _____

_____

7. studying child thinking _____

_____

8. will sentence the criminal _____

_____

Apply What You Know

Use the pronunciations, the part of speech labels, and the definitions given below to write ten new words. Each word uses one of the silent letter combinations you learned in this lesson. Use a dictionary to check your answers.

1. _____ (kam pān′) **n.** a series of organized, planned actions for a purpose such as electing a candidate

2. _____ (sut′ ′l) **adj.** not obvious

3. _____ (säm) **n.** a sacred song; hymn

4. _____ (plum′ ər) **n.** a worker who installs and repairs pipes

5. _____ (get′ ō) **n.** a section of a city where many members of a minority group live

6. _____ (ôt′ əm) **n.** the season between summer and winter; fall

7. _____ (rīm) **n.** correspondence of end sounds in words or lines of poetry

8. _____ (kwäm) **n.** a feeling of uneasiness arising from a consciousness that one is or may be acting wrongly

9. _____ (nô) **v.** to bite and wear away bit by bit with the teeth

10. _____ (poin′ yənt) **adj.** emotionally touching or moving

Proofreading Practice

Proofread these humorous song lyrics. Mark the mistakes in grammar, capitalization, punctuation, and spelling.

Im indebbted to that plummer who soldered my broken heart,

and to his Gnu who nawed its way through my apple tart.

I have no dout that this little tune will some day be maligned,

But its got a good ryhthm, and it's certainly one of a kind.

How many words in the song contain silent letter combinations? _____

Spelling Master 8

Suffixes following hard and soft c/g

elegant	magnificent
communicable	eligible
ambiguous	suspicious
vengeance	innocence

It is sometimes difficult to choose between the following endings: *-ant/-ent, -able/-ible, -uous/-ious, -ance/-ence.*

When the letters *c* and *g* have a hard sound, use the endings *-ance, -ant, -able, -uous.*
Examples: communicable   ambiguous

When the letters *c* and *g* have a soft sound, use the endings *-ence, -ent, -ible, -ious.*
Examples: magnificent   eligible

Note that the final silent *e* is sometimes kept to retain the soft sound of *c* or *g* when a suffix is added.

Practice the Words
Answer each question with a sentence that includes a spelling word. The underlined words will give you a clue to the word you should use.

1. Was the accused man able to prove that he did not <u>commit the crime</u>?

_____

2. What grade point average must a student have to <u>qualify</u> for the team?

_____

3. Was the mansion decorated in a <u>refined and luxurious</u> style?

_____

4. Why do you <u>suspect</u> Billy of having done something wrong?

_____

5. Are impressions easily <u>put into words</u>?

_____

6. Do you think John intended for his comments to be <u>unclear</u>?

_____

7. In the movie why did the cowboy seek <u>retaliation</u>?

_____

8. Which city's skyline do you think is the most <u>grand and impressive</u>?

_____

Apply What You Know

Decide whether the *c* or *g* in each completed word will have a hard or soft sound. Then circle the suffix you would add and write the complete word on the line.

1. neglig +   *-ance* or *-ence*   = _____

2. extravag +   *-ance* or *-ence*   = _____

3. complac +   *-ant* or *-ent*   = _____

4. applic +   *-ant* or *-ent*   = _____

5. invinc +   *-able* or *-ible*   = _____

6. applic +   *-able* or *-ible*   = _____

7. navig +   *-able* or *-ible*   = _____

8. intang +   *-able* or *-ible*   = _____

Proofreading Practice

Proofread this fund-raising letter. Mark the mistakes in grammar, capitalization, punctuation, and spelling.

Dear Friend of Nature,

The Snow leopard is one of the most magnificant animals on earth. It's

heavy pale gray coat keeps it warm and enables it to travel inconspicuous

in the Himalayas. But negligance, extravagence, and complacancy is

bringing this irreplaceible creature to the verge of extinction. You see,

poachers are killing the snow leaopard for its fur. A coat made from this

rare leopard's pelt will sell for over $30,000. You can help stop the illegal

poaching of animals such as the snow leopard by sending us your

contribution today.

Spelling Master 9

Latin and Greek plurals

basis	bases
diagnosis	diagnoses
analysis	analyses
crisis	crises
fungus	fungi
stimulus	stimuli
radius	radii
medium	media
criterion	criteria
	data

> Some words that come from Latin or Greek do not follow English rules for forming the plurals. These words still use the Latin or Greek plural form.
>
> Common usage has almost eliminated the appearance of the Latin singular of some words, such as **datum.**

Practice the Words

Complete each sentence with a spelling word. Circle **S** or **P** to show whether you chose a singular or plural word.

1. The Smith family has experienced a series of _____; a pipe broke and flooded the basement, a storm damaged the roof, and the fire department had to rescue the family cat from a tree. (**S or P**)

2. Mushrooms and other forms of _____ grow abundantly in these woods. (**S or P**)

3. The committee members sent out a survey to collect _____ before they voted on the issue. (**S or P**)

4. The area of a circle is calculated by using a formula that includes the length of the circle's _____. (**S or P**)

5. A chemical _____ of water reveals that it is made up of two colorless gases, hydrogen and oxygen. (**S or P**)

6. The judges agree that balanced composition and use of color are the _____ they will use to choose a winner.(**S or P**)

7. What is the _____, or foundation, of his argument? (**S or P**)

8. Both reward and punishment are great _____ for getting work acomplished. (**S or P**)

9. After studying my symptoms and analyzing my tests, the doctor gave me her _____. (**S or P**)

10. A telephone is considered a _____ of communication. (**S or P**)

Apply What You Know

Listed below are singular forms of twelve more words that come from Latin or Greek.
Use your dictionary to help you write both the singular and plural forms of the words
below. Write them under the categories listed. The first one has been done for you.

| stadium | appendix | agenda | oasis | hypnosis | alumnus |
| aquarium | octopus | axis | vacuum | nucleus | index |

Words that form plurals by
adding **-s**

1. _____stadium—stadiums_____

2. _____

3. _____

4. _____

Words that form plurals by
adding **-es**

5. _____

6. _____

7. _____

Words that form plurals by
changing **is** to **es**

8. _____

9. _____

10. _____

Words that form plurals by
changing **us** to **i**

11. _____

12. _____

Proofreading Practice

Proofread the job description that follows. Mark the mistakes in grammar, capitalization,
punctuation, and spelling.

The general practitioner, or G.P. is often called the family doctor.

General practioners care for all kinds of illnesses, from treating simple

fungis infections to removing appendexes. To identify an illness, a G.P.

usually examine a patient and performs tests. He or she then use the test

results and other datae as the basis for his or her diagnoses. A G.P. may

treat a patient with drugs, or in a crises, may refer a patient to a Specialist.

Spelling Master 10
Words from the French language

tourist   restaurant
souvenir   chauffeur
limousine   lieutenant
silhouette   soldier
coupon   surgeon
gourmet   pigeon

Spelling follows certain patterns in every language. The vowel combinations *ou, au,* and *ie* occur in many words taken from the French language. The *ou* combination most frequently appears in a first syllable.

Only words from the French use the *geon* ending. They cause spelling problems because the *ge* sounds like the *dge* in many English words: fudge judge.

Practice the Words

Complete these analogies. Determine the relationship between the original pair of words. Then write the spelling word that completes the second pair and expresses a relationship similar to the first pair.

1. **Study** is to **school** as **dine** is to _____.

2. **Plane** is to **pilot** as **limousine** is to _____.

3. **Dog** is to **collie** as **bird** is to _____.

4. **Sport** is to **fan** as **food** is to _____.

5. **Hammer** is to **carpenter** as **scalpel** is to _____.

6. **Price** is to **discount** as **bill** is to _____.

7. **Beginner** is to **novice** as **sightseer** is to _____.

8. **Frame** is to **painting** as **outline** is to _____.

9. **Chief** is to **firefighter** as **officer** is to _____.

10. **Vegetable** is to **broccoli** as **vehicle** is to _____.

11. **Currency** is to **money** as **memento** is to _____.

12. **Sheriff** is to **deputy** as **colonel** is to _____.

Apply What You Know

Complete each of these ten words from French. The letters in each word appear scrambled inside the parentheses. Use a dictionary if you need help.

1. c __ r __ __ s __ l   (elsuorac)   HINT: found at amusement park

2. p __ __ __ t __ __   (tporuyl)   HINT: fowl, such as chickens

3. d __ __ g __ __ __   (neoungd)   HINT: found in a castle

4. cr __ __ t __ __ s   (tnsooucr)   HINT: used on salads

5. m __ __ s __ e   (sesumo)   HINT: a type of whipped dessert

6. a __ __ __ st __ cs   (sticscoua)   HINT: related to sound

7. c __ m __ __ fl __ g __   (afelgomacu)   HINT: to blend with the background

8. b __ __ l __ v __ rd   (adlvobuer)   HINT: a broad, well-made street

9. ch __ __ d __ l __ __ r   (ileedrcnah)   HINT: a fancy lighting fixture

10. r __ nd __ z __ __ __ s   (dzevsourne)   HINT: a secret meeting

Proofreading Practice

Proofread this travel itinerary. Mark the mistakes in grammar, capitalization, punctuation, and spelling.

Congratulations! You have just winned a weekend in Paris! On Friday at noon, a limosine will take you from the Paris airport to your hotel. At 6:00 P.M. your private chaffeur will take you to Julienne's, a gourmet restaraunt along Boulevard St.-Michel. We recommend you try the roast pigion with cruotons or the cheese soufflé On Saturday and Sunday you can shop for soveniers along the banks of the Seine river. Or visit the Palace of the Louvre. Show the enclosed copoun in the museum shop to receive a gift. We hope you will enjoy your visit!

Lesson 1
Cuisine

All the words in this lesson may be associated with preparing and eating food.

appliance   N. a piece of household equipment (A toaster is a small *appliance* that is found in many kitchens.)

beverage   N. any liquid for drinking, usually excluding water (Harold's favorite *beverage* is lemonade.)

caldron   N. a large metal container for boiling (In the *caldron* bubbled gallons of hearty soup.)

canister   N. a small box or can for holding a dry product (Please fill the *canister* with flour.)

casserole   N. a dish in which food can be baked and served (Tanya spooned the macaroni into the *casserole* and put it in the oven to bake.)

condiment   N. something used to make food more flavorful (Ketchup was served as a *condiment* for the hamburgers.)

convenience   N. anything that saves time and effort (It is a *convenience* to have a grocery store nearby.)

custard   N. a baked or boiled mixture of eggs, milk, sugar, and flavoring (For dessert we had *custard* with berries on top.)

delicatessen   N. a store that sells ready-to-eat food products (At the neighborhood *delicatessen* we can buy roast beef sandwiches and potato salad.)

gruel   N. a thin porridge made by boiling meal in water or milk (The oatmeal was cooked into a watery *gruel* for the hungry children.)

gumbo   N. a soup thickened with okra and usually containing other vegetables and meat or seafood (Uncle Joe's seafood *gumbo* is a popular dish at his restaurant.)

mash   V. to make into a soft, pulpy mixture (When the potatoes are cooked, you can *mash* them with a large fork.)

mince   V. to cut into very small pieces (Use a sharp knife to *mince* the garlic.)

palatable   ADJ. acceptable to the taste (The chicken was *palatable,* but not delicious.)

pare   V. to remove or cut off the outer layer or skin (Use a knife or peeler to *pare* the apple.)

perishable   ADJ. liable to spoil or decay (Even *perishable* foods can be preserved for several days in the refrigerator.)

permeate   V. to spread throughout (When you cook the cabbage, its strong smell may *permeate* the house.)

saute   V. to brown or cook quickly in an open pan (When the pan is hot, add butter and *saute* the mushrooms for several minutes.)

voracious   ADJ. greedily hungry for great amounts of food (I hope this huge meal will satisfy your *voracious* appetite.)

whet   V. stimulate or sharpen (Before a meal, a walk in the fresh air will often *whet* your appetite and make your food taste better.)

Exercise 1
Write the letter of the word set that best completes the sentence.

1. The good smells from the _____ may _____ your appetite for lunch.
   A. canister — saute
   B. appliance — pare
   C. delicatessen — whet
   D. convenience — mince

2. Put the _____ items in the _____ and refrigerate them.
   A. palatable — custard
   B. palatable — convenience
   C. voracious — caldron
   D. perishable — canister

3. Odors from the wizard's _____ began to _____ the castle.   _____
   A. caldron — permeate   C. canister — mince
   B. beverage — pare   D. caldron — mash

4. If you _____ the onions, we can use them as a _____ for the fish.   _____
   A. mash — canister   C. whet — casserole
   B. mince — condiment   D. permeate — custard

5. The ____ was still _____ even though it was overcooked.   _____
   A. gumbo — voracious   C. custard — palatable
   B. beverage — perishable   D. canister — voracious

6. Pour the leftover _____ into the _____.   _____
   A. delicatessen — caldron   C. beverage — condiment
   B. canister — custard   D. gumbo — casserole

7. A warm _____ may decrease your _____ appetite.   _____
   A. custard — perishable   C. beverage — voracious
   B. appliance — voracious   D. convenience — perishable

8. For the stew, you should _____ the carrots and _____ them in a small amount of   _____
   butter.
   A. pare — saute   C. whet — saute
   B. saute — mince   D. mash — pare

9. Please stir the pot of _____ and _____ a banana for the baby's breakfast. _____
   A. mince — gumbo   C. permeate — beverage
   B. gruel — mash   D. whet — canister

10. In Grandma's time, any electrical _____ was a _____.   _____
   A. canister — casserole   C. appliance — caldron
   B. appliance — convenience   D. casserole — condiment

Exercise 2

Write the letter of the word that most nearly has the *same* meaning as the italicized word.

11. *mash*	A. hide	B. reach	C. crush	D. heat	_____
12. *caldron*	A. kettle	B. dish	C. dessert	D. recipe	_____
13. *casserole*	A. beater	B. sauce	C. dish	D. pitcher	_____
14. *gruel*	A. message	B. plate	C. porridge	D. detergent	_____
15. *whet*	A. copy	B. decrease	C. fade	D. stimulate	_____
16. *saute*	A. boil	B. freeze	C. divide	D. fry	_____
17. *custard*	A. plastic	B. pudding	C. fruit	D. cake	_____
18. *mince*	A. chop	B. fry	C. rinse	D. blend	_____
19. *canister*	A. bowl	B. lid	C. container	D. color	_____
20. *pare*	A. clean	B. peel	C. taste	D. cook	_____

Lesson 2
Law

All the words in this lesson may be associated with the field of law.

admonition N. a gentle warning (The judge's *admonition* quickly quieted the courtroom.)

attorney N. a person legally authorized to act for another (At the trial, an *attorney* represented the accident victim.)

circumstantial ADJ. depending on circumstances; indirectly related (We have nothing definite against the suspect—only *circumstantial* evidence.)

confidential ADJ. secret; private (Most court records are *confidential* and not open to the public.)

conjecture V. to form an opinion without evidence; to guess (I can *conjecture* that the man had a reason to steal the money, but I cannot prove it.)

convict V. to find a person guilty of a crime (Because the stolen money was found in the man's house, the jury will probably *convict* him of the robbery.)

custody N. the right to care for or guard (Both parents wanted *custody* of their child.)

discrimination N. unfairness toward a particular group of persons (There was no *discrimination* in the club because everyone was treated with equal respect.)

disinherit V. to take away the right to receive property from someone who has died (The father was so angry that he threatened to *disinherit* his son.)

divorce N. the legal termination of a marriage (After the *divorce* was final, the husband and wife were no longer married under the law.)

entitle V. to give a claim or right to (Her new position as judge will *entitle* her to make decisions in the courtroom.)

inequity N. something that is not fair or just (Many feel that it is an *inequity* that wealthy people can afford to hire better lawyers.)

injunction N. a court order or command (The judge ordered an *injunction* against selling the land.)

juror N. one of a group of people sworn to hear evidence and make a decision about a law case (Among the eight members of the jury, only one *juror* believed that the woman was guilty.)

juvenile ADJ. characteristic of children or young people (Since the girl was under 18, her case was tried in the *juvenile* court.)

nullify V. to make legally void; to cancel out (The manager warned the team that participating in a players' strike would *nullify* their contracts.)

premeditated ADJ. planned beforehand (Plans were made well in advance for the *premeditated* robbery.)

unwittingly ADV. without being aware of (The lawyer *unwittingly* angered the judge with his excited presentation.)

uphold V. to support or maintain (The Supreme Court will *uphold* the lower court's decision.)

verdict N. a decision reached by a jury at a trial's end (The jury's *verdict* was that the man was guilty.)

Exercise 1
Write the letter of the word that best completes the sentence.

1. The police officer has sworn to _____ the law.
   A. entitle   B. uphold   C. conjecture   D. disinherit   _____

2. Because the evidence was only _____, the man could not be proven guilty.
   A. circumstantial   B. null   C. juvenile   D. confidential   _____

3. The woman had _____ of her brother because he could not take care of himself. _____
   A. injunction   B. discrimination   C. verdict   D. custody

4. A court _____ was necessary to stop the lumber company from cutting down the   _____
   trees.
   A. juror   B. divorce   C. injunction   D. discrimination

5. The jury will announce the _____ after they have discussed the case.   _____
   A. attorney   B. verdict   C. divorce   D. custody

6. The embarrassed driver listened to the policeman's _____ to drive more slowly.   _____
   A. admonition   B. attorney   C. inequity   D. juror

7. The millionaire plans to _____ his children and leave his fortune to his cats.   _____
   A. entitle   B. uphold   C. conjecture   D. disinherit

8. No reporters are allowed to hear the _____ discussions of the jury.   _____
   A. circumstantial   B. confidential   C. null   D. juvenile

9. The worker hit the man in a fit of anger, so it was not a _____ crime.   _____
   A. circumstantial   B. confidential   C. premeditated   D. null

10. The law will not allow an individual to lose a job because of _____.   _____
    A. admonition   B. juror   C. injunction   D. discrimination

11. The courtroom is no place for _____ behavior.   _____
    A. juvenile   B. null   C. circumstantial   D. confidential

12. The evidence against the suspect is so strong that the jury will probably _____   _____
    him.
    A. conjecture   B. convict   C. uphold   D. entitle

13. Both the buyer and the seller agreed to _____ the contract on the house.   _____
    A. juvenile   B. circumstantial   C. nullify   D. premeditated

14. Unfortunately, the court reporter's promotion does not _____ him to a raise.   _____
    A. convict   B. entitle   C. disinherit   D. uphold

15. Because there were so few facts in the case, we could only _____ about what   _____
    really happened.
    A. convict   B. uphold   C. entitle   D. conjecture

Exercise 2
Write the letter of the word pair that has a relationship similar to the relationship of the
first word pair.

16. *attorney : courtroom : :*   A. policeman : criminal   C. guilty : innocent   _____
                                     B. doctor : hospital   D. wishing : hoping

17. *inequity : justice : :*   A. courtroom : judge   C. light : dark   _____
                                     B. small : tiny   D. chapter : novel

18. *unwittingly : unknowingly : :* A. death : life   C. law : enforce   _____
                                     B. doctor : patient   D. habit : custom

19. *jury : juror : :*   A. camera : picture   C. cold : ice   _____
                                     B. team : player   D. robin : bird

20. *divorce : marriage : :*   A. tall : short   C. run : skip   _____
                                     B. pebble : stone   D. judge : jury

Lesson 3
Money and Finance

All the words in this lesson may be associated with the field of finance.

absolute ADJ. whole; without a doubt (The bank needs *absolute* proof of your identity.)

accumulate V. to gather together; collect (Over the next few years, Sarah will *accumulate* a large sum of money from her investments.)

additional ADJ. extra; added (John will have *additional* income from his second job.)

advisable ADJ. reasonable or proper under the circumstances (It is not *advisable* to borrow money when interest rates are high.)

apportionment N. the act of dividing and distributing according to a plan (In the *apportionment* of Grandfather's fortune every family member received a small amount.)

approve V. to consent to something (If the bank official can *approve* their loan application by 5:00 today, then they will have the money by tomorrow morning.)

competitive ADJ. trying to win or gain something over another (A *competitive* store owner may use low prices to attract shoppers.)

corporation N. a business organization that operates independently from the individuals who own or manage it (The electronics *corporation* offered free child-care for its employees.)

counterfeit ADJ. imitation; fake (The *counterfeit* dollar looked real.)

currency N. the money used in a country (In the United States, you cannot buy something using *currency* from another country.)

deduct V. to take away from the total (To calculate your profit, you should *deduct* your expenses from your total earnings.)

discrepancy N. lack of agreement or consistency (There is a *discrepancy* between what you think you should be paid and what you actually earned.)

endorse V. to write one's signature; to sign (You *endorse* a check by writing your name on the back of it.)

forgery N. the imitation of a signature or document with the intent to deceive (The signature was a *forgery* because the wrong person had written it.)

gross ADJ. total; with nothing subtracted (She will need to set aside money for taxes from her *gross* income.)

installment N. one of a series of payments (Joe will pay for the bike with a $25 *installment* each month.)

itemize V. to write down item by item; to list (If you want to *itemize* your expenses, keep a record of everything you spend.)

leverage N. an advantage in position (Jan's public speaking experience gave her *leverage* in her sales presentation.)

percentage N. a portion or part of a whole (A large *percentage* of his income is spent on videos.)

solvent ADJ. able to pay all debts (The company was *solvent* because it took in more money than it spent.)

Exercise 1
Write the letter of the word that best completes the sentence.

1. The _____ of the bake sale money was decided by the class. _____
   A. corporation   B. forgery   C. apportionment   D. leverage

2. Please use a pen to _____ the check. _____
   A. endorse   B. deduct   C. accumulate   D. itemize

3. The large _____ had offices in many cities. _____
  A. currency   B. forgery   C. percentage   D. corporation

4. We needed to know more, so the bank provided _____ information. _____
  A. additional   B. counterfeit   C. solvent   D. advisable

5. He has some _____ within the company because he is the owner's son. _____
  A. percentage   B. leverage   C. installment   D. forgery

6. When we traveled, we found it difficult to change from one country's _____ to _____
  another's.
  A. corporation   B. forgery   C. installment   D. currency

7. After expenses were subtracted from her _____ income, she had very little _____
  money.
  A. gross   B. counterfeit   C. solvent   D. advisable

8. On Friday you should pay the first _____ on the loan for your new computer. _____
  A. forgery   B. corporation   C. leverage   D. installment

9. Please use this record book to _____ your expenses for the trip. _____
  A. endorse   B. itemize   C. accumulate   D. approve

10. If you compare the two signatures, you can tell that one is a _____. _____
  A. percentage   B. currency   C. forgery   D. installment

Exercise 2
Write the letter of the word that most nearly has the *opposite* meaning as the italicized
word.

11. *percentage*   A. profit   B. expense   C. all   D. half   _____

12. *discrepancy*   A. agreement   B. time   C. crime   D. figure   _____

13. *absolute*   A. uncertain   B. enough   C. tired   D. wasted   _____

14. *deduct*   A. subtract   B. hold   C. add   D. buy   _____

15. *solvent*   A. successful   B. flat   C. incorrect   D. bankrupt   _____

16. *accumulate*   A. bring   B. win   C. scatter   D. defeat   _____

17. *competitive*   A. cooperative   B. unfair   C. lucky   D. high   _____

18. *approve*   A. reduce   B. offer   C. deny   D. subtract   _____

19. *counterfeit*   A. formal   B. profitable   C. low   D. genuine   _____

20. *advisable*   A. right   B. unwise   C. complex   D. changed   _____

Lesson 4
School Days

All the words in this lesson may be associated with school.

diploma   N. a certificate given by a school to its graduating students (Juan's *diploma* stated that he had graduated from the eighth grade.)

distribute   V. to divide and give out in shares (The teacher will *distribute* colored markers and poster paper to the class.)

enrollment   N. the number of persons who are members (Three new students joined our class, so our *enrollment* has increased.)

extracurricular   ADJ. not part of the regular course of study (You do not get a grade for playing in the band because it is an *extracurricular* activity.)

idle   ADJ. not busy; doing nothing (There are so many problems to do that no one should be *idle* during math period.)

intellectual   ADJ. having to do with the mind (His *intellectual* interests include studying philosophy and reading history books.)

interruption   N. a break in an action (The fire drill was an *interruption* in our class routine.)

intramural   ADJ. limited to participants from the same school (Room 127 will play Room 234 in the *intramural* basketball game.)

mascot   N. a person, animal, or thing meant to bring good luck (Our school's *mascot* is a bulldog.)

nominate   V. to name a candidate for office (Each homeroom will *nominate* someone to run in the election for class president.)

procession   N. a group of persons or things moving forward in an orderly way (The *procession* of candidates walked slowly toward the stage.)

provocation   N. a cause of anger or irritation (The students' constant giggling was the *provocation* for our teacher's outburst.)

rapport   N. a relationship based on trust and understanding (The principal is well-liked and has an excellent *rapport* with her students.)

registration   N. the process of being recorded on a list (You may sign up for summer school during today's *registration*.)

reprimand   V. to scold severely (Ms. Thomas will *reprimand* you if your homework is not completed.)

rowdy   ADJ. rough and disorderly (The crowd of *rowdy* students bumped into people as they ran down the hall.)

scrutiny   N. close examination (My report looks fine, but under *scrutiny* it shows signs of being hastily written.)

summarize   V. to give the main points of (One way to study for a history test is to *summarize* each paragraph of the chapter.)

suspension   N. a period in which operations or activities are stopped (The student was not allowed to attend class during his *suspension* from school.)

undergraduate   N. a student, especially in a college or university (She studied English literature during the four years of her *undergraduate* education.)

Exercise 1

Write the letter of the word that best completes the sentence.

1. Mark wants to _____ his best friend for class treasurer.   _____
   A. distribute   B. nominate   C. reprimand   D. summarize

2. Some students want the school _____ to be a tiger.   _____
   A. mascot   B. scrutiny   C. diploma   D. suspension

3. The doctor has his medical school _____ hanging on the wall.   _____
   A. enrollment   B. rapport   C. interruption   D. diploma

4. Only students from our school can play in the _____ volleyball tournament.   _____
   A. rowdy   B. intellectual   C. intramural   D. idle

5. Not one _____ disturbed the students during the test.   _____
   A. interruption   B. rapport   C. mascot   D. enrollment

6. Lois cannot play on the tennis team because she has no time for _____ activities.   _____
   A. idle   B. extracurricular   C. intellectual   D. rowdy

7. Since the _____ is so high, Mr. Jones must offer two sections of the cooking   _____
   class.
   A. interruption   B. undergraduate   C. mascot   D. enrollment

8. A freshman or sophomore will be the _____ representative on the college board.   _____
   A. rowdy   B. scrutiny   C. undergraduate   D. mascot

9. The coach has good _____ with the players on the soccer team.   _____
   A. mascot   B. provocation   C. procession   D. rapport

10. The library is no place for _____ behavior.   _____
    A. extracurricular   B. intramural   C. rowdy   D. intellectual

11. Only in extreme cases does the principal recommend _____ from school as a   _____
    punishment.
    A. enrollment   B. procession   C. rapport   D. suspension

12. The _____ of graduating students stretched along the length of the gym.   _____
    A. diploma   B. suspension   C. provocation   D. procession

13. Please _____ the important points of today's biology lesson before the bell rings.   _____
    A. summarize   B. reprimand   C. distribute   D. nominate

14. Rita is in charge of the _____ of voters for the class election.   _____
    A. interruption   B. registration   C. diploma   D. undergraduate

15. Use the microscope for close _____ of this strand of hair.   _____
    A. enrollment   B. suspension   C. scrutiny   D. registration

Exercise 2

Write the letter of the word pair that has a relationship similar to the relationship of the
first word pair.

16. *idle : busy : :*   A. asleep : awake   C. happy : joyful   _____
                               B. dog : bone   D. dish : spoon

17. *reprimand : scold : :*   A. fish : water   C. head : mouth   _____
                               B. close : shut   D. hard : rock

18. *intellectual : mind : :*   A. house : hut   C. tool : sharp   _____
                               B. physical : body   D. shiny : dull

19. *distribute : papers : :*   A. dark : night   C. cool : ice   _____
                               B. color : sky   D. plant : seeds

20. *provocation : anger : :*   A. flame : heat   C. driver : car   _____
                               B. king : subject   D. hold : carry

Lesson 5
Feelings

All the words in this lesson may be associated with feelings.

adolescence   N. the period of physical and psychological growth following childhood (During *adolescence,* many twelve and thirteen year olds experience extreme mood changes.)

animosity   N. hatred that is shown openly (Even though Greg disliked the bus driver, he showed no *animosity* toward him.)

annoyance   N. a feeling of trouble or irritation (It was an *annoyance* to carry the heavy basket, but it did not spoil the picnic.)

apprehensive   ADJ. fearful about what may happen (Because he forgot to study, Jerome is *apprehensive* about tomorrow's test.)

chagrin   N. a feeling of failure or disappointment in oneself (Pam did not show her *chagrin* at losing the race, but everyone knew she felt bad.)

defiance   N. refusal to obey (Sally showed her *defiance* of the rules by deliberately breaking them.)

devoid   ADJ. completely lacking (My little brother is *devoid* of all table manners.)

disconsolate   ADJ. extremely sad; unable to be comforted (Even though her friends tried to cheer her up, Lisa was *disconsolate* after she had lost her kitten.)

dissatisfied   ADJ. not content (The *dissatisfied* customer complained to the manager about the bad food.)

emotion   N. a strong feeling (People sometimes show the *emotion* of happiness by dancing.)

empathy   N. a sharing of another's feelings without going through the same experiences (The caring rescue worker could feel *empathy* for the flood victims' desperate situation.)

envious   ADJ. feeling resentment because of the qualities or achievements of another (Bob was in a bad mood because he was *envious* of his brother's success.)

exuberance   N. being high-spirited and joyous (The cheerleaders' *exuberance* increased the fans' enthusiasm.)

futility   N. uselessness (She will give up when she realizes the *futility* of her efforts.)

negative   ADJ. expressing a denial or refusal; not constructive (Carmen's *negative* attitude toward the class caused her to perform poorly in that subject.)

passion   N. strong or intense feeling (Our science teacher spoke with great *passion* of the need to protect our environment.)

sensitive   ADJ. responsive to the feelings or attitudes of others (A mother's *sensitive* ear can tell when a child is hurt.)

serenity   N. quiet peace; calmness (The *serenity* of the peaceful scene was disturbed by the loud honking of a car horn.)

uncertainty   N. doubt (Because she disliked cold water, Lana paused with *uncertainty* at the end of the diving board.)

wretched   ADJ. feeling miserable (Toby felt *wretched* after his poor performance at the recital.)

Exercise 1
Write the letter of the word that best completes the sentence.

1. Although Eli enjoyed his own family, he felt _____ for his good friend whose home life was unhappy.   _____
   A. exuberance   B. serenity   C. empathy   D. animosity

2. The teacher could not hide her _____ at the constant interruptions.   _____
   A. annoyance   B. serenity   C. adolescence   D. empathy

3. Since Corinne is not used to speaking before large crowds, she is _____ about her upcoming speech. _____
   A. devoid   B. apprehensive   C. disconsolate   D. sensitive

4. We will welcome the _____ of the quiet countryside after the noise and confusion of the city. _____
   A. adolescence   B. emotion   C. animosity   D. serenity

5. In her _____, she knocked a vase from the table. _____
   A. empathy   B. adolescence   C. exuberance   D. serenity

6. The child showed his _____ of authority by kicking and screaming. _____
   A. defiance   B. empathy   C. serenity   D. adolescence

7. Bill finally realized the _____ of trying to train the stubborn dog. _____
   A. serenity   B. futility   C. exuberance   D. emotion

8. His tired speeches are boring and lack _____ and enthusiasm. _____
   A. uncertainty   B. chagrin   C. passion   D. animosity

9. Eve was _____ of her friend's achievement and wished that she had won the prize instead. _____
   A. devoid   B. envious   C. sensitive   D. negative

10. Rely on reason rather than _____ when making your decision. _____
    A. adolescence   B. chagrin   C. animosity   D. emotion

Exercise 2

Write the letter of the word that most nearly has the *opposite* meaning of the italicized word.

11. **sensitive**	A. loud	B. unfeeling	C. happy	D. helpful	_____
12. **wretched**	A. happy	B. sick	C. sad	D. tired	_____
13. **chagrin**	A. leadership	B. ignorance	C. satisfaction	D. brilliance	_____
14. **animosity**	A. sickness	B. cruelty	C. perfection	D. love	_____
15. **adolescence**	A. adulthood	B. program	C. training	D. stupidity	_____
16. **dissatisfied**	A. discontent	B. limp	C. pleased	D. sincere	_____
17. **uncertainty**	A. concern	B. confidence	C. rudeness	D. question	_____
18. **disconsolate**	A. comforted	B. strict	C. confused	D. furious	_____
19. **negative**	A. unsure	B. useless	C. positive	D. perfect	_____
20. **devoid**	A. truthful	B. alone	C. unkind	D. full	_____

Lesson 6
Writing and Editing

All the words in this lesson may be associated with the processes of writing and editing.

abbreviation N. a shortened form of a word or phrase (An *abbreviation* is usually followed by a period.)

abridge V. to make shorter by using fewer words (If we *abridge* the story, it will not take as many pages.)

arduous ADJ. hard to do (The computer helps with the *arduous* task of checking for misspelled words.)

classify V. to organize according to some method or system (Please *classify* the books according to their authors.)

clause N. a group of words containing a subject and a verb (A *clause* is not always a complete sentence.)

conjugation N. a systematic arrangement of the forms of a verb (The *conjugation* of the verb "to have" includes "I have, you have, he has, we have, you have, they have.")

duplicate V. to make another exactly like the original (If Grover can *duplicate* the drawing, we will have two copies.)

enclosure N. something put into an envelope along with a letter (The photograph was an *enclosure* that came with the letter.)

gazette N. a publication, usually issued daily or weekly, containing current news, editorials, and advertisements (Our local *gazette* contains too many advertisements and too little news.)

hyphen N. a punctuation mark used to connect parts of a compound word or between syllables at the end of a line (There is a *hyphen* in the word "thirty-four.")

incomprehensible ADJ. not able to be understood (A sentence can be *incomprehensible* when it lacks proper punctuation.)

indentation N. the blank space between the margin and a line that has been set in (A new paragraph is indicated by an *indentation* at the beginning.)

informative ADJ. providing information (We learned facts about Antarctica from her *informative* report.)

isolate V. to set apart from others (Jana will *isolate* herself from family and friends until she finishes writing her story.)

italics N. a printing style with the letters slanting to the right (Titles of books should be underlined or placed in *italics*.)

leaflet N. a small, folded sheet of printed matter (She received a *leaflet* in the mail today about the annual writers' convention.)

logical ADJ. reasonable (Because of his writing experience, James is the *logical* choice for editor of the newspaper.)

pseudonym N. a name used by an author instead of his or her real name (Mrs. Harris uses a male *pseudonym* when she writes detective novels.)

publisher N. a person or company that produces and distributes printed material (We must get permission from the *publisher* to reprint the story.)

stationery N. writing materials such as paper, cards, and envelopes (We bought Mother colorful *stationery* and matching pens for her birthday.)

Exercise 2
Write the letter of the word set that best completes the sentence.

1. Learning about the _____ of verbs can be an _____ task.
   A. italics — logical
   B. pseudonym — informative
   C. conjugation — arduous
   D. enclosure — incomprehensible

2. The _____ will accept Cindi's lengthy article only if she will _____ it. _____
   A. gazette — abridge
   B. leaflet — isolate
   C. clause — classify
   D. enclosure — duplicate

3. Capitalize the _____ at the beginning of the _____. _____
   A. hyphen — enclosure
   B. leaflet — gazette
   C. indentation — pseudonym
   D. abbreviation — clause

4. The _____ message written on her father's _____ puzzled her. _____
   A. incomprehensible — stationery
   B. informative — conjugation
   C. arduous — hyphen
   D. logical — abbreviation

5. Throughout the _____, the _____ of each paragraph should be the same. _____
   A. gazette — conjugation
   B. leaflet — indentation
   C. abbreviation — italics
   D. clause — publisher

6. The librarian's _____ talk explained the system used to _____reference books. _____
   A. incomprehensible — abridge
   B. logical — duplicate
   C. arduous — isolate
   D. informative — classify

7. The _____ place to use a _____ is between syllables. _____
   A. logical — hyphen
   B. arduous — gazette
   C. informative — publisher
   D. incomprehensible — pseudonym

8. Please _____ the _____ before sealing the envelope. _____
   A. abridge — conjugation
   B. duplicate — enclosure
   C. isolate — leaflet
   D. classify — italics

9. The _____ wanted the author to use a(n) _____ instead of her real name. _____
   A. gazette —indentation
   B. leaflet — enclosure
   C. clause — conjugation
   D. publisher — pseudonym

10. John could not get his printer to type _____ until the repairman was able to
    _____ the cause and fix the problem. _____
    A. abbreviation — abridge
    B. gazette — duplicate
    C. italics — isolate
    D. stationery — classify

Exercise 2

Write the letter of the word that most nearly has the *same* meaning as the italicized word.

11. *arduous*	A. handy	B. false	C. difficult	D. regular	_____
12. *duplicate*	A. stay	B. copy	C. punish	D. promise	_____
13. *leaflet*	A. headline	B. answer	C. volume	D. pamphlet	_____
14. *abridge*	A. shorten	B. close	C. solve	D. arrange	_____
15. *gazette*	A. newspaper	B. envelope	C. photograph	D. movie	_____
16. *classify*	A. delay	B. close	C. lengthen	D. arrange	_____
17. *stationery*	A. paper	B. publisher	C. gazette	D. stable	_____
18. *isolate*	A. win	B. separate	C. persuade	D. believe	_____
19. *informative*	A. tiny	B. educational	C. boring	D. brief	_____
20. *logical*	A. unusual	B. expensive	C. sensible	D. long	_____

Lesson 7
Construction

All the words in this lesson may be associated with construction.

alcove   N. A small room or recess opening off a larger room (In the *alcove* just off the living room, there is space for a small table and a reading chair.)

asbestos   N. a fireproof material made of mineral fibers (The roofing materials are made of *asbestos* to resist heat.)

ample   ADJ. of great size or capacity; roomy (There was room for many clothes as well as a dresser in the *ample* closet space.)

atrium   N. a hall or courtyard at the center of a building (All of the windows in that house face the *atrium.*)

clearance   N. the act of removing (The crew will begin *clearance* of the fallen trees from the hillside by first hauling away the branches.)

cubicle   N. a very small room or compartment (Father built a *cubicle* in which to store his gardening equipment.)

drainage   N. gradual flowing off (The house on the hill will not flood because the hill provides natural *drainage* for rainwater.)

elaborate   ADJ. having many details; worked out with great care (Even electrical outlets were shown on the *elaborate* design plan.)

facade   N. the front part of a building (From the street the building's *facade* looked shabby, but inside the rooms were freshly painted.)

faulty   ADJ. having errors; falling short of perfection (He was warned that the *faulty* wiring could cause a fire.)

hovel   N. a house that is small, miserable, and unpleasant to live in (Although the house was nothing more than a *hovel,* the land on which it stood was valuable.)

inlaid   ADJ. set in the surface as a decoration or design (The dark oak door has an *inlaid* design of light wood.)

insulation   N. material used to keep from losing or transferring heat, sound, or electricity (New *insulation* will not let the warm air escape through the walls of the house.)

pulley   N. a grooved wheel on which a rope or chain can pull; used to lift heavy loads (Use a *pulley* to lift the heavy lumber to the second floor.)

renovate   V. to make new again (The historical society plans to *renovate* the old railroad station by putting on a new roof and painting the outside.)

residential   ADJ. containing or suitable for homes (No office buildings can be built within the *residential* area.)

scrimp   V. to be very sparing with; to cut down on (The contractor should not *scrimp* on good quality materials if she wants to do a high quality job.)

solder   V. to join two metal surfaces together with a melted substance (To make the connection, he will *solder* the two wires together by melting lead with a heated iron rod.)

specification   N. a detailed description of materials, quantities, and sizes needed (Once the *specification* is complete, the cost of the lumber can be estimated.)

ventilate   V. to circulate fresh air in (Please open the window to *ventilate* the room.)

Exercise 1
Write the letter of the word that best completes the sentence.

1. The plans for the large office building must include _____ parking space. _____
   A. faulty   B. residential   C. inlaid   D. ample

2. The washing machine and dryer were in a small _____ next to the kitchen. _____
   A. facade   B. cubicle   C. specification   D. pulley

3. Along the balcony there was _____ iron work with complicated designs. _____
   A. elaborate   B. faulty   C. residential   D. hovel

4. Because of the smell, the painter will _____ the room while she is working. _____
   A. scrimp   B. renovate   C. solder   D. ventilate

5. There were many small homes in the _____ part of town. _____
   A. residential   B. faulty   C. ample   D. inlaid

6. You can put the television in the _____ off the study. _____
   A. asbestos   B. insulation   C. alcove   D. clearance

7. The building looked new after the brickwork on the _____ had been cleaned. _____
   A. pulley   B. specification   C. hovel   D. facade

8. Set into the wooden surface of the coffee table was a(n) _____ pattern made of _____
   ivory and jade.
   A. inlaid   B. ample   C. faulty   D. residential

9. The _____ of rocks and brush from the property will take several days of hard _____
   work.
   A. insulation   B. atrium   C. hovel   D. clearance

10. Due to the use of _____ throughout the building, there was little fire damage. _____
   A. asbestos   B. cubicle   C. facade   D. alcove

11. From the _____, the builder can determine the size of the deck. _____
   A. pulley   B. drainage   C. specification   D. asbestos

12. A _____ was used to move their grand piano into the upstairs apartment. _____
   A. cubicle   B. pulley   C. facade   D. specification

13. The valley had no _____, so flooding was a problem. _____
   A. insulation   B. pulley   C. cubicle   D. drainage

14. Plans for the _____ showed placement of plants and a skylight. _____
   A. atrium   B. hovel   C. cubicle   D. asbestos

15. In order to afford a new house, the Smiths must _____ on buying furniture. _____
   A. renovate   B. scrimp   C. ventilate   D. solder

Exercise 2

Write the letter of the word pair that has a relationship similar to the relationship of the first word pair.

16. **solder : wires : :**   A. concrete : cement   C. glue : papers   _____
                        B. bakery : bread   D. house : garage

17. **renovate : building : :**   A. recycle : newspapers   C. sun : shine   _____
                        B. tall : ladder   D. jog : run

18. **insulation : house : :**   A. pages : book   C. door : garage   _____
                        B. hammer : nail   D. coat : person

19. **hovel : shack : :**   A. sister : brother   C. attic : cellar   _____
                        B. mistake : error   D. wagon : automobile

20. **faulty : fault : :**   A. exploding : explosion   C. hard : soft   _____
                    B. ladder : climb   D. fire : fireplace

Lesson 8
Sports

All the words in this lesson may be associated with sports.

adept   ADJ. skillful; expert (Her strength and speed make Maurine an *adept* tennis player.)

admittance   N. the right to enter (To gain *admittance* to the game you have to buy a ticket.)

bicker   V. to argue over an unimportant matter (If players begin to *bicker*, the coach will stop the argument by sending them to the locker room.)

brawny   ADJ. strong; muscular (The *brawny* fullback can carry one of the smaller players down the field.)

confidence   N. firm belief in oneself and one's abilities (Anna gained *confidence* as she won game after game.)

contend   V. to take part in a contest (Three of the school's best runners will *contend* in the first race.)

devise   V. to think out; plan (Our coach will *devise* some new plays for Saturday's game.)

falter   V. to pause because of doubt; to lose courage (The crowd saw the lead runner *falter* and then leave the race because of a pulled muscle.)

footwork   N. use of management of the feet (We watched the boxer's fancy *footwork* as he danced around the ring.)

forfeit   V. to lose or have to give up as a penalty (Unless the rest of our players arrive soon, we will have to *forfeit* the game to the other team.)

incapable   ADJ. lacking the necessary ability or training (Although James is *incapable* of running long distances, he is a swift sprinter.)

lunge   V. to move forward suddenly (The crowd watched the outfielder *lunge* for the ball and then catch it in his outstretched glove.)

monumental   ADJ. having great size; very large (The *monumental* stadium covered ten acres.)

morale   N. the state of mind of a person or group as shown by cheerfulness and confidence (You could tell from their enthusiastic faces that the players' *morale* was high.)

motivation   N. an incentive to strive or perform well (The hope of getting a college scholarship was George's *motivation* for practicing gymnastics every day.)

penalty   N. punishment or disadvantage for breaking a rule (The *penalty* for arguing with the umpire is being thrown out of the game.)

plaque   N. a decorated or engraved plate, slab, or disk usually given in honor of someone or something (When they won the tournament, the team received a *plaque* that now hangs in the school's hallway.)

solitary   ADJ. alone; single (All we could see on the field was the *solitary* figure of the coach.)

substitution   N. putting one person or thing in the place of another (A *substitution* can only be made during a timeout.)

victor   N. the winner of a contest or competition; the conqueror (A silver trophy will be presented to the *victor* of today's tennis championship.)

Exercise 1
Write the letter of the word that best completes the sentence.

1. Team _____ was low until Coach Ko gave an encouraging pep talk.   _____
   A. penalty   B. morale   C. plaque   D. victor

2. Our star pitcher will _____ a way to strike out the opponent's home run hitter.   _____
   A. devise   B. lunge   C. bicker   D. forfeit

3. An anxious runner may _____ forward before the starting whistle blows.   _____
   A. bicker   B. forfeit   C. devise   D. lunge

4. The coach will make a _____ for the injured player.   _____
   A. footwork   B. confidence   C. substitution   D. morale

5. Winning the game is a strong _____ for playing well.   _____
   A. admittance   B. victor   C. penalty   D. motivation

6. We will have to _____ the game if we do not have the correct uniforms.   _____
   A. bicker   B. forfeit   C. lunge   D. contend

7. Only those players wearing rubber-soled shoes were allowed _____ onto the   _____
   basketball court.
   A. substitution   B. admittance   C. confidence   D. penalty

8. The quarterback's quick _____ made him difficult to tackle.   _____
   A. victor   B. penalty   C. footwork   D. plaque

9. The winning coach proudly hung the _____ in the trophy case.   _____
   A. plaque   B. motivation   C. confidence   D. substitution

10. If we are to _____ in the play-offs, we must win all of our remaining games.   _____
    A. bicker   B. devise   C. lunge   D. contend

Exercise 2

Write the letter of the word that most nearly has the *opposite* meaning of the italicized
word.

11. *brawny*	A. quick	B. strange	C. weak	D. easy	_____
12. *victor*	A. king	B. loser	C. uniform	D. position	_____
13. *penalty*	A. prize	B. trick	C. coach	D. moment	_____
14. *solitary*	A. strong	B. quiet	C. slow	D. multiple	_____
15. *confidence*	A. power	B. shyness	C. happiness	D. wealth	_____
16. *falter*	A. continue	B. delay	C. stop	D. wait	_____
17. *bicker*	A. race	B. dance	C. release	D. agree	_____
18. *adept*	A. unskilled	B. formal	C. peaceful	D. willing	_____
19. *monumental*	A. ugly	B. beautiful	C. small	D. stone	_____
20. *incapable*	A. proud	B. able	C. tired	D. bored	_____

Lesson 9
Behavior

All the words in this lesson may be associated with behavior.

agonize   V. to suffer greatly (Charles will *agonize* over the difficult decision.)

amiable   ADJ. friendly or pleasing (The *amiable* hostess greeted her guests and made them feel welcome.)

apathetic   ADJ. showing little interest or concern (Although most of us were excited about the project, Carmen was an *apathetic* student who did not seem to care.)

attentive   ADJ. paying attention; alert (Those who were *attentive* during the lecture heard the speaker mispronounce the principal's name.)

compulsive   ADJ. in a manner resulting from a strong urge (Aunt Kim is a *compulsive* eater who eats all the time when she is nervous or worried.)

congenial   ADJ. agreeable; pleasant (Dave is fun to be with because he is such a *congenial* person.)

consequence   N. something that results from an earlier action (As a *consequence* of misbehaving, Ivan had to stay after class.)

defy   V. to resist openly and boldly (You will *defy* your father if you say that you are staying out after midnight.)

disrespect   N. lack of courtesy or respect (You can show *disrespect* for an older person when you do not listen to what he or she is saying.)

elated   ADJ. in high spirits (Jumping up and down with excitement, Andy was obviously *elated* by the team's victory.)

excessive   ADJ. more than necessary; extremely (Bowing to your dinner guests would probably be considered *excessive* politeness.)

exclude   V. to keep out (Since boys were not allowed in their club, the girls voted to *exclude* their little brothers from club meetings.)

extrovert   N. an active, outgoing person (The *extrovert* talked to everyone in sight.)

gravitate   V. to move toward or be attracted to (Because they tend to *gravitate* toward one another, new students often become friends.)

impulse   N. a sudden driving force or influence (Although he had not planned to call his parents, an *impulse* led him to pick up the phone.)

incompatible   ADJ. not able to interact in a friendly manner (You could tell that Janet and Ellen were *incompatible* because they fought all the time.)

ingrate   N. a person who is not appreciative (Without a word of thanks, the *ingrate* left with his gift.)

levity   N. lightness in manner or speech (There should be no joking or *levity* during a solemn ceremony.)

ridicule   V. to make fun of (In speech class, no one is allowed to laugh at or *ridicule* the speaker.)

temperamental   ADJ. sensitive or moody (You could tell by the way she stomped her foot and stormed off that she was a *temperamental* person.)

Exercise 1
Write the letter of the word that best completes the sentence.

1. The sick child had lost interest in reading books and was _____ about his toys.   _____
   A. incompatible   B. apathetic   C. excessive   D. congenial

2. Some people are _____ shoppers and buy items that they really don't need.   _____
   A. congenial   B. compulsive   C. elated   D. amiable

3. The fascinated children were _____ during the movie.   _____
   A. attentive   B. incompatible   C. ingrate   D. consequence

4. For showing _____ to the boss, Miles lost his job.   _____
   A. extrovert   B. disrespect   C. ingrate   D. consequence

5. Amy invited the whole class to the party because she did not want to _____   _____
   anyone.
   A. gravitate   B. ridicule   C. agonize   D. exclude

6. He never spoke in school because he was afraid other students would _____ him   _____
   for his strange accent.
   A. ridicule   B. gravitate   C. agonize   D. exclude

7. Although the senator joked at the beginning of his speech, there was no _____ in   _____
   his voice as he described the conditions of the homeless.
   A. extrovert   B. impulse   C. levity   D. ingrate

8. The passengers were greeted with a smile from the _____ bus driver.   _____
   A. incompatible   B. amiable   C. apathetic   D. compulsive

9. Mark found that the _____ of not studying was a low test grade.   _____
   A. impulse   B. consequence   C. ingrate   D. disrespect

10. Sue moved out of the room because she and her roommate were _____.   _____
    A. attentive   B. apathetic   C. compulsive   D. incompatible

11. After working hard on her paper, Maria was _____ when she got an A.   _____
    A. amiable   B. elated   C. excessive   D. temperamental

12. Although she had not planned to purchase anything, a sudden _____ made her   _____
    buy the dress.
    A. extrovert   B. ingrate   C. impulse   D. disrespect

13. Jan had assignments for every class, but she did not feel that there was a(n)   _____
    _____ amount of homework.
    A. compulsive   B. amiable   C. excessive   D. temperamental

14. Because they have so much in common, the two doctors will _____ toward each   _____
    other at the banquet.
    A. exclude   B. gravitate   C. agonize   D. defy

15. Su Lyn cannot make up her mind, and will _____ over even a small decision.   _____
    A. gravitate   B. exclude   C. ridicule   D. agonize

Exercise 2

Write the letter of the word pair that has a relationship similar to the relationship of the
first word pair.

16. **congenial : disagreeable : :**   A. dirty : clean   C. hateful : mean   _____
                                        B. hand : glove   D. less : least

17. **defy : rebel : :**   A. stand : sit   C. pout : smile   _____
                            B. carry : haul   D. run : race

18. **extrovert : talkative : :**   A. baby : tall   C. door : hallway   _____
                                     B. whistle : shrill   D. man : dog

19. **ingrate : thankful : :**   A. house : paint   C. rain : dry   _____
                                  B. tree : old   D. freezer : cold

20. **unstable : temperamental : :**   A. repair : ruin   C. humor : humorous   _____
                                        B. care : caring   D. happy : glad

Lesson 10
Nature and Wildlife

All the words in this lesson may be associated with nature and wildlife.

abundant   V. to be plentiful (Although now only several hundred remain, buffalo used to be *abundant* on America's western plains.)

aviary   N. a house or large cage for birds (We saw many varieties of birds as we walked through the *aviary* at the zoo.)

binoculars   N. a double telescope for both eyes, used to magnify distant objects (With *binoculars* we could see into the fox's den on the faraway hillside.)

colossal   ADJ. huge; gigantic (A *colossal* snowslide covered the buildings at the ski resort.)

confine   V. to keep within limits (The fire fighters tried to *confine* the forest fire to a small area.)

conservationist   N. one who works toward the preserving of natural resources (The *conservationist* did not approve of cutting down forest trees.)

cypress   N. a cone-bearing evergreen tree (On our trip to Florida we saw a *cypress* growing out of the swamp.)

dislodge   V. to move or force out of position (The rock was wedged between two trees, but we were able to *dislodge* it, using a stick for a lever.)

envelop   V. to wrap up or cover completely (Early in the morning, fog will *envelop* the mountain peaks so that they cannot be seen.)

ferocious   ADJ. cruel; fierce (Although bears are not usually *ferocious* animals, they may become dangerous when they are hungry.)

forestry   N. the science of planting and taking care of forests (Lin studied *forestry* in college because she wanted to become a park ranger.)

hardy   ADJ. strong; able to withstand harsh conditions (The spring snowstorm did not affect the *hardy* wildflowers.)

indigenous   ADJ. of a species originally living in a region rather than being brought in from outside the region (The wild turkey is *indigenous* to North America.)

innocuous   ADJ. causing no harm (The small berry looked *innocuous,* but it was actually highly poisonous.)

instinct   N. a natural feeling or knowledge (Although humans must learn how to make their shelters, a bird builds a nest by *instinct*.)

lair   N. the den or resting place of a wild animal (The lion usually makes its *lair* in a rocky cave.)

lessen   V. to make less; decrease (Loud talking on the trail will frighten animals away and *lessen* your chances of seeing wildlife.)

persistent   ADJ. refusing to give up (The *persistent* bird watcher sat for five hours waiting to see the bald eagle leave its nest.)

swampy   ADJ. like soft wet land (Ducks and geese feed in ponds in the *swampy* area near the river.)

vegetation   N. plant life (The lack of *vegetation* on the mountain meant there was little food for the animals.)

Exercise 1
Write the letter of the word that best completes the sentence.

1. Ducks learn to swim by _____.   _____
    A. vegetation   B. instinct   C. forestry   D. binoculars

2. Climbers who _____ rocks make it dangerous for hikers below.   _____
    A. dislodge   B. envelop   C. lessen   D. confine

3. A degree in _____ will qualify a graduate to work in any national park. _____

   A. aviary   B. cypress   C. instinct   D. forestry

4. Through the _____ we can see the bird's unusual markings. _____

   A. binoculars   B. conservationist   C. forestry   D. instinct

5. Small birds darted through the air in the _____ at the zoo. _____

   A. instinct   B. cypress   C. aviary   D. binoculars

6. Every year birds flock to the old _____ to build their nests. _____

   A. forestry   B. conservationist   C. cypress   D. instinct

7. The _____ met with city council to discuss preserving wetlands near the bay. _____

   A. cypress   B. vegetation   C. lair   D. conservationist

8. Although it took hours, the _____ ant dragged the crumb of food to the anthill. _____

   A. persistent   B. colossal   C. swampy   D. indigenous

9. The color of the _____ changes from green to red and orange in the fall. _____

   A. conservationist   B. vegetation   C. aviary   D. lair

10. The wolf cubs were left in the _____ while the parents hunted for food. _____

   A. cypress   B. conservationist   C. lair   D. forestry

Exercise 2

Write the letter of the word that most nearly has the *opposite* meaning of the italicized word.

11. *confine*	A. release	B. capture	C. hold	D. hide	_____
12. *abundant*	A. sweet	B. scarce	C. live	D. fat	_____
13. *indigenous*	A. inside	B. costly	C. common	D. foreign	_____
14. *colossal*	A. tiny	B. mysterious	C. humane	D. single	_____
15. *envelop*	A. unwrap	B. send	C. carry	D. find	_____
16. *hardy*	A. tall	B. colorful	C. weak	D. harmful	_____
17. *swampy*	A. dreary	B. grassy	C. dry	D. high	_____
18. *innocuous*	A. careful	B. harmful	C. silly	D. tasty	_____
19. *ferocious*	A. unhappy	B. mild	C. ugly	D. rude	_____
20. *lessen*	A. shrink	B. teach	C. delay	D. increase	_____

Lesson 11
Mystery and Suspense

All the words in this lesson may be associated with solving mysteries.

bewilderment   N. state of being puzzled and unclear (His *bewilderment* increased as the clues led nowhere.)

cryptogram   N. a message written in code (In the *cryptogram,* the number 5 stood for the letter *e.*)

disagreement   N. a failure to agree; a difference of opinion (Their argument in public was proof of the *disagreement* between them.)

endanger   V. to expose to danger (He may not live long, because knowledge of the secret may *endanger* his life.)

evident   ADJ. easy to see or understand (It was *evident* that she was in a hurry because she was walking so fast.)

feign   V. to pretend; to give a false appearance of (Sometimes the murderer will *feign* surprise when he hears of the victim's death.)

flask   N. any bottle-shaped container (In the chemist's laboratory, the *flask* of mysterious liquid steamed.)

fraught   ADJ. filled with or accompanied by (Going into the abandoned house at night was *fraught* with danger.)

homicide   N. the killing of one human being by another (Although the death was ruled a *homicide,* it may be that the man fell by accident.)

identical   ADJ. the same (You could not tell the *identical* necklaces apart.)

identity   N. who a person is (The thief concealed her *identity* with a mask and a wig.)

imprint   N. a mark made by pressure (The *imprint* in the sand had been made by a two-wheeled vehicle.)

inscription   N. words or characters written, carved, or engraved on a surface (With a sharp rock, the boy scratched a short *inscription* on the tombstone.)

intrigue   V. to excite curiosity or interest (If the clues in the case *intrigue* you, you may want to hear more.)

mystify   V. to confuse or bewilder (Several false clues were planted to mislead and *mystify* the police.)

password   N. a secret word or phrase that identifies the speaker (When she said the *password,* she was allowed to enter the secret chamber.)

persist   V. refuse to stop or be changed (Sherlock Holmes will *persist* in looking for clues until the mystery is solved.)

premise   N. a statement assumed to be true and used to draw a conclusion (The detective's case is based on the *premise* that no shots were fired.)

systematic   ADJ. having a system or method (Everyone's duties were carefully outlined in the *systematic* investigation.)

uncanny   ADJ. arousing wonder and fear; mysterious (She was troubled by the *uncanny* feeling that something was wrong.)

Exercise 1
Write the letter of the word set that best completes the sentence.

1. The _____ plan that was used to steal the crown jewels will _____ the police department for many years.
   A. fraught — mystify   C. evident — feign
   B. systematic — intrigue   D. identical — persist   _____

2. William knew about the _____ but he continued to _____ ignorance.
   A. disagreement — persist   C. cryptogram — endanger
   B. bewilderment — mystify   D. homicide — feign   _____

3. Since the _____ had no markings, there was _____ about its origin. _____
   A. flask — disagreement   C. password — imprint
   B. inscription — identity   D. cryptogram — homicide

4. The _____ noises from the locked house continued to _____ the detectives. _____
   A. evident — persist   C. uncanny — mystify
   B. fraught — intrigue   D. systematic — feign

5. The incorrect _____ given at the door will _____ the undercover agent. _____
   A. homicide — mystify   C. disagreement — feign
   B. password — endanger   D. flask — persist

6. Although the _____ appeared to be a man's, the detective will _____ in _____
   questioning all family members.
   A. imprint — persist   C. inscription — mystify
   B. identity — endanger   D. cryptogram — intrigue

7. Based on the _____ that the butler was a murderer, the other servants were _____
   _____ with fear.
   A. disagreement — evident   C. bewilderment — uncanny
   B. password — intrigue   D. premise — fraught

8. Because the _____ on each dagger was _____, they all looked alike. _____
   A. password — systematic   C. inscription — identical
   B. flask — evident   D. bewilderment — uncanny

9. The carefully constructed _____ gave no clue to the _____ of its author. _____
   A. homicide — imprint   C. imprint — password
   B. inscription — premise   D. cryptogram — identity

10. From the suspect's _____, it was _____ that he did not know the answer. _____
    A. identity — fraught   C. disagreement — systematic
    B. bewilderment — evident   D. inscription — identical

Exercise 2

Write the letter of the word that most nearly has the *same* meaning as the italicized word.

11. **uncanny**   A. heroic   B. strange   C. difficult   D. easy   _____

12. **mystify**   A. chase   B. locate   C. inform   D. puzzle   _____

13. **evident**   A. obvious   B. grand   C. expensive   D. calm   _____

14. **feign**   A. neglect   B. clean   C. flush   D. fake   _____

15. **systematic**   A. antique   B. clean   C. orderly   D. mysterious _____

16. **identical**   A. alike   B. beautiful   C. proper   D. unusual   _____

17. **disagreement** A. excitement B. quarrel   C. relationship   D. observation _____

18. **intrigue**   A. fascinate   B. anger   C. follow   D. find   _____

19. **bewilderment** A. happiness   B. argument   C. horror   D. confusion   _____

20. **persist**   A. continue   B. listen   C. lighten   D. cancel   _____

Lesson 12
Clothing and Fashion

All the words in this lesson may be associated with clothing and fashion.

acrylic ADJ. a man-made textile fiber that resembles wool, but when woven makes a lightweight, wrinkle-resistant fabric (Although the *acrylic* blanket is lightweight, it keeps the baby warm.)

alter V. to make different; change (The tailor can *alter* the suit by shortening the skirt.)

cardigan N. a collarless sweater that opens down the front (There are pearl buttons on the red wool *cardigan* that Mother wears with her plaid skirt.)

elegant ADJ. tastefully rich, as in dress or furnishings (Mona's simple but *elegant* black dress was perfect for the party.)

flamboyant ADJ. brightly colorful; showy (Juan will surely attract attention by wearing this *flamboyant* shirt.)

flammable ADJ. easily set on fire (No *flammable* fabrics should be used for children's clothing.)

frill N. a gathered piece of fabric or lace used as decoration; ruffle (The *frill* around the skirt's hem was made of antique lace.)

indigo ADJ. deep violet-blue (The *indigo* dress matched her deep blue eyes.)

informal ADJ. suitable for everyday use or casual occasions (We can wear comfortable, casual clothing to an *informal* party.)

iridescent ADJ. showing a shimmering, changing display of rainbowlike colors (The *iridescent* pearl buttons shimmered in the candlelight.)

lapel N. a flap that results from a fold in the front of a coat below the neckline (Father wore a red rosebud in the buttonhole of his *lapel*.)

maroon ADJ. dark purplish red (A *maroon* tie will add color to your dark gray suit.)

miscellaneous ADJ. of different kinds; made up of a variety (On the sale rack were shirts, pants, belts, and other *miscellaneous* items.)

reduction N. the act of making smaller or less (There will be a *reduction* in the price of all dresses at the store's spring sale.)

rustle V. to make a soft, fluttering sound (As she walked, you could hear the *rustle* of her long silk skirt.)

scorch V. to burn on the surface (Shannon will *scorch* her blouse if she does not lower the temperature of the iron.)

specify V. to state details clearly (Please *specify* the size and the color you would like when you order from a catalogue.)

stationary ADJ. having a fixed position; not moving (The model remained *stationary* for several minutes so the customers could view her outfit.)

tassel N. a hanging ornament consisting of a bunch of small cords or threads bound together at one end (A gold *tassel* hung from the right shoulder of each band member's uniform.)

vat N. a large container for holding liquids (The fabric was dropped into a steaming *vat* of purple dye.)

Exercise 1
Write the letter of the word that best completes the sentence.

1. Millie's outfit is too _____ for the quiet, formal gathering.
   A. indigo   B. stationary   C. flamboyant   D. flammable   _____

2. With the exception of the new _____ drapes, everything in the room is blue.
   A. maroon   B. indigo   C. miscellaneous   D. stationary   _____

3. To reduce the danger of fire, any _____ products are safely stored on the top shelf _____
   in the garage.
   A. elegant   B. flammable   C. indigo   D. maroon

4. The homemade jacket has one _____ that is wider than the other.   _____
   A. lapel   B. cardigan   C. reduction   D. vat

5. The candle will _____ the wallpaper if it is placed too close.   _____
   A. rustle   B. alter   C. specify   D. scorch

6. A lacy _____ around the bottom of the dress was the finishing touch.   _____
   A. frill   B. vat   C. lapel   D. cardigan

7. Ricardo discovered that a _____ was missing from one of the laces on his loafers.   _____
   A. lapel   B. tassel   C. cardigan   D. reduction

8. We bought _____ fabric because it would not wrinkle.   _____
   A. informal   B. indigo   C. acrylic   D. miscellaneous

9. Please remain _____ until the picture is taken.   _____
   A. maroon   B. stationary   C. flammable   D. indigo

10. The hotel's expensive quilts are washed in a _____ of special detergent.   _____
    A. frill   B. lapel   C. vat   D. tassel

11. During the review session our teacher will _____ exactly what the test covers.   _____
    A. scorch   B. rustle   C. specify   D. alter

12. Bring a _____ because the weather will be cool.   _____
    A. frill   B. vat   C. cardigan   D. tassel

13. Either sky-blue or _____ is my favorite shade of blue.   _____
    A. acrylic   B. iridescent   C. flamboyant   D. indigo

14. Emma's large, _____ earrings seemed to reflect the spotlight.   _____
    A. iridescent   B. flammable   C. stationary   D. miscellaneous

15. We could tell from the _____ furnishings that the owner was wealthy.   _____
    A. stationary   B. elegant   C. acrylic   D. flammable

Exercise 2

Write the letter of the word pair that has a relationship similar to the relationship of the
first word pair.

16. *alter : dress : :*   A. finish : start   C. sleep : baby   _____
                                 B. remodel : house   D. change : vary

17. *rustle : leaves : :*   A. chime : bell   C. run : athlete   _____
                                   B. drive : car   D. read : student

18. *reduction : lower : :*   A. bank : money   C. special : ordinary   _____
                                     B. joke : funny   D. increase : raise

19. *informal : relaxed : :*   A. happy : sad   C. king : subject   _____
                                      B. smooth : even   D. difficult : problem

20. *miscellaneous : identical : :*   A. plant : field   C. damp : dry   _____
                                             B. late : tardy   D. painter : brush

Lesson 13
Travel

All the words in this lesson may be associated with travel.

alpine   ADJ. having to do with high mountains (The travelers were promised mountain scenery and clean, fresh air on the *alpine* tour.)

ascend   V. to move upward (We watched a daring mountain climber *ascend* the steep slope.)

bazaar   N. a marketplace in Middle and Far Eastern countries including one or more streets lined with shops (At the Moroccan *bazaar* we bought inexpensive gifts for the whole family.)

charter   V. to lease or hire by contract (The travel club will *charter* a cruise ship for touring the islands.)

cordiality   N. warmth; friendliness (The innkeeper's *cordiality* made us feel welcome in the strange surroundings of a new country.)

detain   V. to hold back; delay (We will be late if the guards *detain* us at the border to search our luggage.)

disembark   V. to put or get off an airplane or ship (The travelers will take their belongings off the boat when they *disembark* in Egypt.)

fiord   N. a long, narrow inlet from the sea between high, steep cliffs, found especially in Norway and Alaska (As the ship entered the *fiord,* the passengers gazed at snow-covered cliffs that rose out of the still water.)

futuristic   ADJ. of the future (*Futuristic* travel posters advertise vacations on other planets.)

identification   N. proof of who a person is (The passport she used for *identification* displayed her photograph and address.)

idyllic   ADJ. relating to the simple, quiet beauty of country life (Lim spends restful weekends in the *idyllic* surroundings of his fishing cabin.)

province   N. a political division of a country (Mother thinks that Alberta is Canada's most beautiful *province*.)

remote   ADJ. located far away (We were miles from populated areas on a *remote* island in the Caribbean.)

shortage   N. a lack in the amount needed (The towel *shortage* meant that there were not enough towels for all the guests.)

spry   ADJ. lively; able to move quickly and lightly (The *spry* old gentleman was first to reach the top of the tower.)

suite   N. a series of connected rooms considered a unit (The hotel *suite* included a bedroom, a living room, and a bath.)

summon   V. to send for or request the presence of (Please *summon* the guests to the ship's dining room.)

unpredictable   ADJ. not sure; with doubt (During hurricane season in the Gulf Coast, the *unpredictable* weather can quickly change vacation plans.)

vacancy   N. empty or unoccupied space (Unfortunately, there was no *vacancy* at the only hotel in town.)

yearn   V. to feel a strong desire or longing (We often *yearn* for the quiet and simple beauty of the European villages.)

Exercise 1
Write the letter of the word that best completes the sentence.

1. The hotel's finest _____ was reserved for the governor.
   A. identification   B. shortage   C. suite   D. fiord

2. We will each pay a dollar so the school can _____ a bus to take our class to the museum. _____
   A. yearn   B. charter   C. ascend   D. disembark

3. Every city in the northern French _____ had a remarkable cathedral. _____
   A. province   B. suite   C. identification   D. vacancy

4. Mr. Chang longs for a snowy, _____ vacation, but his wife does not want to go to the mountains. _____
   A. futuristic   B. unpredictable   C. spry   D. alpine

5. They welcomed him with great _____, even though he could not speak their language. _____
   A. shortage   B. bazaar   C. cordiality   D. fiord

6. There were many fish in the icy waters of the _____. _____
   A. identification   B. fiord   C. bazaar   D. suite

7. The motel had only one _____ left when we called for reservations. _____
   A. bazaar   B. shortage   C. province   D. vacancy

8. The _____ charm of the seaside community was destroyed when it was chosen as the site for filming a new movie. _____
   A. alpine   B. futuristic   C. idyllic   D. spry

9. Many colorful stalls of the _____ lined the street near our hotel. _____
   A. fiord   B. bazaar   C. shortage   D. charter

10. The tour guide warned the travelers to carry _____ at all times in case of an emergency. _____
    A. identification B. cordiality   C. bazaar   D. vacancy

Exercise 2

Write the letter of the word that most nearly has the *opposite* meaning of the italicized word.

11. *unpredictable*	A. peculiar	B. certain	C. shaky	D. improbable	_____
12. *ascend*	A. allow	B. hire	C. descend	D. predict	_____
13. *disembark*	A. board	B. address	C. believe	D. save	_____
14. *remote*	A. nearby	B. impossible	C. alone	D. frantic	_____
15. *spry*	A. inactive	B. attentive	C. clean	D. healthy	_____
16. *yearn*	A. simplify	B. follow	C. pay	D. dislike	_____
17. *detain*	A. support	B. respect	C. hurry	D. stop	_____
18. *futuristic*	A. intense	B. energetic	C. silly	D. antique	_____
19. *summon*	A. believe	B. dismiss	C. want	D. call	_____
20. *shortage*	A. snip	B. need	C. abundance	D. list	_____

Lesson 14
Government

All the words in this lesson may be associated with government.

agitator   N. a person who causes discontent in an effort to change things (The political *agitator* turned the crowd against the speaker.)

communist   ADJ. characterized by a system of government in which a single political party controls the government, production and distribution of goods (In a *communist* country, all property belongs to the state.)

confederacy   N. a group of persons or states joined together for a purpose (The European states were organized into a *confederacy* to encourage trade.)

confer   V. to discuss together (There were heated discussions when the leaders of the five countries met to *confer* about world affairs.)

constituent   N. a voter represented by elected officials (The senator tried to speak for each *constituent* in his state.)

decline   N. a lessening or decreasing (The *decline* of the king's power meant that he no longer had the authority to raise taxes.)

delegation   N. a group given the authority to act or speak for others (Two men and three women were in the *delegation* that the country sent to the peace conference.)

depress   V. to lower prices; to make less profitable (Having too many houses available will *depress* the housing market.)

dictator   N. a person who rules a country with complete power and authority (The *dictator* had the final say in all decisions.)

distribution   N. the act of dividing and handing out goods (The agency in charge of food *distribution* sent grain to needy countries.)

emigrant   N. someone who leaves a country to settle in another country (The poet was an *emigrant* who had left his country for political reasons.)

equatorial   ADJ. close to the equator (In *equatorial* Africa, the weather is very hot.)

incumbent   N. a person holding an elected office (The *incumbent* will run for another term in office.)

interact   V. to act with each other; to have an effect on one another (World peace depends on how countries *interact* with each other.)

naturalize   V. to accept as a citizen of a country (If the government agrees to *naturalize* the girl from Mexico, she will become an American citizen.)

politician   N. a person who holds or runs for public office (The *politician* promised her supporters that she would lower taxes if elected.)

presidential   ADJ. having to do with the president (During the *presidential* address, the president outlined his new plan for education.)

tariff   N. taxes on imported or exported goods (The *tariff* on the car from Japan made it more expensive.)

territorial   ADJ. having to do with a specific region or territory (The country's *territorial* waters included any part of the ocean within one hundred miles of its shoreline.)

veto   V. to use the power of a president or chief executive to stop a bill passed by the legislature (If the President should *veto* the bill, it will not become a law.)

Exercise 1
Write the letter of the word that best completes the sentence.

1. In the United States, a _____ election is held every four years.   _____
   A. depressive   B. presidential   C. communist   D. equatorial

2. In Washington, there was a special ceremony to _____ new citizens.   _____
   A. confer   B. interact   C. naturalize   D. veto

3. After hearing the rousing speech of the _____, the crowd became excited and demanded action from the government. _____
   A. tariff   B. agitator   C. confederacy   D. decline

4. The country had _____ rights in the areas near its borders. _____
   A. communist   B. presidential   C. equatorial   D. territorial

5. If the two leaders can _____ well together, they will work on joint projects in the future. _____
   A. interact   B. veto   C. naturalize   D. depress

6. After she left her native country, the _____ felt lost. _____
   A. emigrant   B. dictator   C. incumbent   D. tariff

7. The tribes in the Indian _____ agreed to hunt only in special areas. _____
   A. agitator   B. constituent   C. confederacy   D. politician

8. The mayor assured his _____ that he would try to improve the city bus program. _____
   A. emigrant   B. politician   C. tariff   D. constituent

9. All the candidates belonged to the same party in the _____ country's election. _____
   A. equatorial   B. communist   C. presidential   D. territorial

10. The _____ had held the office for ten years. _____
    A. tariff   B. delegation   C. incumbent   D. emigrant

Exercise 2

Write the letter of the word that most nearly has the *same* meaning as the italicized word.

11. *tariff*	A. sheriff	B. tax	C. fine	D. location	_____
12. *confer*	A. talk	B. dance	C. affect	D. allow	_____
13. *depress*	A. lower	B. correct	C. find	D. try	_____
14. *veto*	A. hang	B. form	C. back	D. reject	_____
15. *dictator*	A. entertainer	B. follower	C. ruler	D. driver	_____
16. *delegation*	A. light	B. committee	C. election	D. host	_____
17. *politician*	A. maid	B. announcer	C. senator	D. assistant	_____
18. *equatorial*	A. single	B. tropical	C. arctic	D. wet	_____
19. *distribution*	A. price	B. mark	C. delay	D. division	_____
20. *decline*	A. decrease	B. seek	C. have	D. inform	_____

Lesson 15
Medicine

All the words in this lesson may be associated with medicine.

adverse   ADJ. not in one's favor; causing injury (Some *adverse* effects of this medicine may include nervousness and loss of sleep.)

antiseptic   ADJ. capable of destroying infection (This *antiseptic* liquid will kill germs in cuts and scratches.)

cleanse   V. to make clean (The nurse will first *cleanse* the wound with soap and water.)

coma   N. being unaware of one's surroundings as a result of injury, disease, or poison (Although the patient seemed to be sleeping, he was in a *coma* and could neither hear nor speak.)

dental   ADJ. of or for the teeth (A yearly *dental* examination should help to prevent tooth decay.)

dilate   V. to make larger; expand (After the doctor uses eye drops to *dilate* your pupil, it takes about an hour for the pupil to return to its normal size.)

donor   N. a person who gives or contributes something (A *donor* has offered a pint of blood for the injured man.)

fitful   ADJ. irregular; going on and then stopping awhile (The child cried out several times during her night of *fitful* sleep.)

immobilize   V. to prevent motion; to fix firmly (A walking cast will not *immobilize* you.)

inability   N. being unable (Carmen must take liquid medicine because of her *inability* to swallow pills.)

infect   V. to transmit a disease to (Billy must stay home from school so he does not *infect* his classmates with the measles.)

lozenge   N. a small tablet of medicine (Sucking on the fruit-flavored *lozenge* will help ease the child's sore throat.)

nausea   N. a feeling of the need to vomit (Jane's *nausea* makes her dislike the sight of food.)

noticeable   ADJ. easily seen or noticed (Everyone remarked on the *noticeable* change in Arthur's energy level since he began taking vitamins.)

pallor   N. paleness caused by illness, fear, or death (Jeff's *pallor* and loss of appetite indicated that he was not feeling well.)

probe   V. to explore a body cavity or wound with a slender surgical instrument (Before stitching the wound, the surgeon will *probe* the cut for splinters of glass.)

relapse   N. becoming ill again after a partial recovery (Because he had left the hospital too soon, he suffered a *relapse* and had to go back to bed.)

supportive   ADJ. providing approval, help, or confidence (The *supportive* therapist encouraged the injured runner to try racing again.)

vial   N. a small glass or plastic bottle for holding liquid (If taken as directed, this *vial* of medicine should last for two weeks.)

virulent   ADJ. poisonous or deadly (No cure has been discovered for the *virulent* disease.)

Exercise 1
Write the letter of the word that best completes the sentence.

1. That dirty bandage may _____ the open wound.   _____
   A. cleanse   B. immobilize   C. infect   D. probe

2. Let the _____ slowly dissolve in your mouth.   _____
   A. lozenge   B. coma   C. pallor   D. vial

3. Use a sterilized needle to gently _____ the wound if you are looking for bits of gravel that may be in the scrape.
   A. infect   B. probe   C. immobilize   D. dilate

4. Suddenly, after months in a(n) _____, Rich opened his eyes.
   A. inability   B. coma   C. vial   D. nausea

5. The _____ lotion will keep the infection from spreading.
   A. dental   B. supportive   C. adverse   D. antiseptic

6. The directions on the glass _____ said to take two teaspoonfuls at bedtime.
   A. lozenge   B. vial   C. donor   D. coma

7. The patient's _____ insurance will cover the cost of all work done to her teeth.
   A. antiseptic   B. dental   C. fitful   D. virulent

8. If the medicine causes headaches or _____, discontinue use and phone the doctor immediately.
   A. nausea   B. vial   C. lozenge   D. donor

9. If the patient does not have a(n) _____, she may leave the hospital next week.
   A. probe   B. relapse   C. cleanse   D. infect

10. A(n) _____ family can give a patient the will to recover quickly.
    A. fitful   B. adverse   C. antiseptic   D. supportive

Exercise 2

Write the letter of the word that most nearly has the *opposite* meaning of the italicized word.

11. *donor*   A. teacher   B. mistake   C. recipient   D. millionaire

12. *noticeable*   A. hidden   B. beautiful   C. sad   D. obvious

13. *inability*   A. happiness   B. belief   C. power   D. opinion

14. *virulent*   A. soft   B. harmless   C. strange   D. frightening

15. *fitful*   A. peaceful   B. lively   C. interrupted   D. frustrating

16. *immobilize*   A. sound   B. judge   C. hold   D. activate

17. *adverse*   A. difficult   B. simple   C. favorable   D. loud

18. *dilate*   A. heal   B. contract   C. open   D. clothe

19. *pallor*   A. color   B. poison   C. sickness   D. support

20. *cleanse*   A. assist   B. climb   C. inspect   D. dirty

Lesson 16
History

All the words in this lesson may be associated with the study of history.

ancestral   ADJ. having to do with those from whom a person is descended (The *ancestral* estate has been in the family for generations.)

armada   N. a fleet of warships (In 1588, an *armada* of 100 Spanish ships was defeated by the British navy.)

armistice   N. an agreement to stop fighting (When the *armistice* was declared, all the countries put down their weapons.)

barbarism   N. a brutal or uncivilized condition or act (The *barbarism* of the attack proved that the soldiers had little respect for human life.)

bicentennial   ADJ. having to do with a 200th anniversary (During the *bicentennial* celebration, we remembered the birth of our country 200 years ago.)

chauvinism   N. blind patriotism (His *chauvinism* did not allow him to see the faults of his country.)

counteract   V. to act against; to neutralize (During the last days of the Roman Empire, free entertainment was provided to *counteract* the citizens' discontent.)

courtship   N. the act or time of seeking the affection of a person with the intent to marry (Long ago men and women could not choose whom to marry because the process of *courtship* was governed by strict rules.)

culminate   V. to reach the end or highest point (The history pageant will *culminate* in the presentation of awards.)

demise   N. death (The country mourned the unexpected *demise* of its leader.)

eliminate   V. to remove or take away (Kings of old would often *eliminate* rivals for the throne by throwing them into prison.)

epoch   N. a period of time; age (The invention of the steam engine marked an *epoch* of industrial progress.)

forebear   N. ancestor (A *forebear* of mine came to this country from Italy in 1890.)

gladiator   N. a slave or paid fighter in the arenas of ancient Rome (The *gladiator* fought wild animals for the amusement of the Roman crowds.)

imprison   V. to confine or put in jail (The government will *imprison* anyone who sells military secrets.)

legendary   ADJ. of or having to do with legends or tales (Paul Bunyan is a *legendary* American hero.)

saber   N. a heavy, curved sword (Every soldier had a wide *saber* belted to his waist.)

sheath   N. a holder or case for a knife or sword (He slipped the hunting knife back into its *sheath* after stabbing the wild boar.)

telegraph   N. a system for sending messages by electric signals through a wire or radio (On a *telegraph*, letters of the alphabet are represented by combinations of short and long signals.)

traitorous   ADJ. like one who betrays his or her country (It was a *traitorous* deed when the soldier told the enemy about the planned surprise attack.)

Exercise 1
Write the letter of the word pair that best completes the sentence.

1. The government will _____ the man for his _____ acts.   _____
   A. culminate — ancestral   C. imprison — traitorous
   B. counteract — legendary   D. counteract — bicentennial

2. The _____ ended the _____ of the war.   _____
   A. armistice — barbarism   C. forebear — epoch
   B. sheath — chauvinism   D. epoch — demise

3. The jeweled _____ held the steel _____ of the general. _____
   A. armada — telegraph
   B. gladiator — forebear
   C. armistice — sheath
   D. sheath — saber

4. The defeat of the _____ at sea would _____ the threat of invasion. _____
   A. armada — eliminate
   B. gladiator — culminate
   C. barbarism — imprison
   D. demise — counteract

5. Our _____ home was passed from one _____ to the next. _____
   A. bicentennial — saber
   B. legendary — gladiator
   C. ancestral — forebear
   D. traitorous — epoch

6. Extreme _____ can lead to the _____ of tolerance. _____
   A. telegram — gladiator
   B. chauvinism — demise
   C. barbarism — armistice
   D. epoch — gladiator

7. A(n) _____ can _____ in marriage. _____
   A. epoch — imprison
   B. saber — eliminate
   C. courtship — culminate
   D. armada — counteract

8. During the _____ celebration, stories were told of the _____ heroes of the _____
   Revolutionary War.
   A. ancestral — bicentennial
   B. bicentennial — legendary
   C. traitorous — legendary
   D. ancestral — traitorous

9. During the _____ of westward expansion in the United States, the _____ was _____
   the chief means of communication.
   A. gladiator — demise
   B. chauvinism — forebear
   C. barbarism — armada
   D. epoch — telegraph

10. A Roman _____ often used a shield to _____ his opponent's attack. _____
    A. saber — imprison
    B. barbarism — culminate
    C. gladiator — counteract
    D. chauvinism — eliminate

Exercise 2

Write the letter of the word that most nearly has the *opposite* meaning of the italicized word.

11. *culminate*	A. begin	B. paint	C. continue	D. try	_____
12. *eliminate*	A. sew	B. create	C. hide	D. insist	_____
13. *demise*	A. comfort	B. hunger	C. birth	D. grave	_____
14. *traitorous*	A. patriotic	B. sick	C. wicked	D. strong	_____
15. *barbarism*	A. alone	B. civility	C. shadow	D. rhythm	_____
16. *armistice*	A. bell	B. government	C. fighting	D. ruler	_____
17. *counteract*	A. forecast	B. vote	C. file	D. encourage	_____
18. *imprison*	A. remove	B. free	C. place	D. burden	_____
19. *chauvinism*	A. pride	B. meeting	C. disloyalty	D. parade	_____
20. *forebear*	A. heir	B. pamphlet	C. officer	D. agency	_____

Lesson 17
Language and Literature

All the words in this lesson may be associated with language and literature.

admirable ADJ. deserving high regard or praise (The hero's kindness, intelligence, and wit are all *admirable* traits.)

classic N. a work of literature or art of the highest quality (Because people have read the book with pleasure for years, Mark Twain's *Tom Sawyer* is considered a *classic*.)

climax N. the turning point or point of highest excitement in a play or novel (We held our breath during the *climax* of the murder mystery.)

delineate V. to sketch or outline; portray (Through a brief history of the feud between the two families, the writer will *delineate* the play's conflict.)

enrich V. to improve or make richer (Reading will *enrich* your life by acquainting you with new ways of looking at the world.)

figurative ADJ. using words for a vivid or dramatic effect rather than for their literal meaning ("It's raining cats and dogs" is *figurative* language.)

imagery N. the use of words to appeal to the senses (The *imagery* of a rosy-fingered dawn helps you visualize an early morning sky.)

improper ADJ. incorrect; not proper ("We done our homework" is an example of *improper* grammar.)

literary ADJ. having to do with literature (Greg's *literary* club meets every Monday night to discuss the books they have read.)

locale N. the setting of a written work (The *locale* of the story is a small, midwestern town during the Depression.)

myth N. a story told in ancient times to explain life and nature (The *myth* of Narcissus examines self-love through the story of a boy who falls in love with his own reflection.)

prologue N. an introduction to a play, novel, or other literary work (The *prologue* gave background information about the main character's childhood.)

scoundrel N. a villain (Although the prince was handsome, he was a *scoundrel* who used others to get what he wanted.)

seminar N. a conference at which information and opinions are exchanged (Ramona plans to attend a *seminar* about writing and selling children's literature.)

stanza N. a section or division of a poem (The first *stanza* is repeated at the end of the ballad.)

symbolize V. to stand for something else (A robin or a flower may *symbolize* spring.)

tendency N. a natural disposition to move, act, or think in a certain way (The author's work needs editing because he has a *tendency* to use run-on sentences.)

translation N. something that is expressed in another language (Only minor details were lost in the *translation* of the story from Japanese to English.)

unravel V. to work out the problems of or make clear (The story's bumbling detective could not *unravel* the mystery.)

unsavory ADJ. unpleasant; having a bad reputation (He was an *unsavory* character with shifty eyes and a violent temper.)

Exercise 1
Write the letter of the word that best completes the sentence.

1. The suspense grew steadily until the _____ of the story.
   A. prologue   B. seminar   C. classic   D. climax   _____

2. She must memorize one _____ of the poem.
   A. scoundrel   B. stanza   C. seminar   D. tendency   _____

3. As the main character travels across America, the _____ of the story changes. _____
    A. seminar   B. classic   C. myth   D. locale

4. A(n) _____ critic described the good and bad points of the book. _____
    A. unsavory   B. literary   C. figurative   D. improper

5. The poet's effective use of _____ language helped to paint a mental picture for _____
    the reader.
    A. improper   B. unsavory   C. figurative   D. admirable

6. A famous Greek _____ attempts to explain the seasonal changes on earth. _____
    A. locale   B. myth   C. climax   D. seminar

7. Our English teacher has the _____ quality of being able to criticize a paper and _____
    praise it at the same time.
    A. figurative   B. unsavory   C. admirable   D. improper

8. Before the first act, the _____ gave details about the town and its citizens. _____
    A. scoundrel   B. prologue   C. tendency   D. seminar

9. Only one _____ from French to English has preserved the rhythm of the poetry. _____
    A. climax   B. tendency   C. translation   D. myth

10. With the use of _____, a writer can make sights and sounds come alive. _____
    A. prologue   B. imagery   C. scoundrel   D. seminar

11. This author has a _____ to describe the characters in too much detail. _____
    A. myth   B. classic   C. translation   D. tendency

12. You should _____ the hero's character through his actions. _____
    A. delineate   B. enrich   C. symbolize   D. unravel

13. The audience was surprised when the handsome, charming main character proved _____
    to be a _____.
    A. locale   B. scoundrel   C. translation   D. prologue

14. Because his novel is so well-written, it may someday be considered a _____. _____
    A. tendency   B. climax   C. seminar   D. classic

15. During the _____, the students discussed Marta's paper on *To Kill a Mockingbird*. _____
    A. seminar   B. motif   C. imagery   D. climax

Exercise 2

Write the letter of the word pair that has a relationship similar to the relationship of the
first word pair.

16. *symbolize : represent : :*   A. disappear : vanish   C. glove : hand   _____
                                         B. income : expense   D. paint : house

17. *enrich : enrichment : :*   A. wise : wisdom   C. enjoy : enjoyment   _____
                                       B. rich : richer   D. miserable : misery

18. *unsavory : honorable : :*   A. round : curved   C. cloudy : clear   _____
                                        B. food : tasty   D. unpleasant : odor

19. *unravel : mystery : :*   A. soothe : quiet   C. sour : sweet   _____
                                     B. follow : march   D. solve : problem

20. *improper : behavior : :*   A. correct : right   C. sloppy : appearance   _____
                                       B. egg : basket   D. easy : difficult

Lesson 18
Transportation

All the words in this lesson may be associated with transportation.

antifreeze   N. a liquid added to water to keep it from freezing (Mix *antifreeze* with the water in your car's radiator so it won't turn to ice in cold weather.)

asphalt   N. a tar-like substance mixed with stone and sand that is used to pave roads (The road crew used hot, black *asphalt* to repair parts of the road.)

conserve   V. to keep and protect from loss; to preserve (If we drive slowly, we will *conserve* fuel and avoid having to stop for more gas.)

coupe   N. a two-door automobile with a closed roof (I can drive five people to the picnic in my new *coupe*.)

dashboard   N. the instrument panel of a car, truck, bus, or other vehicle (Check the speedometer on the *dashboard* to see if we are going too fast.)

exceed   V. go beyond (If you *exceed* the speed limit, you may be stopped by a policeman for going too fast.)

horsepower   N. unit for measuring the power of motors and engines (An engine of two hundred *horsepower* was needed to move the heavy train.)

inflate   V. to fill with air or gas (You can use the tire pump to *inflate* the tire as soon as we have repaired the leak.)

intersection   N. the place where one street crosses another (I'll meet you at the *intersection* of Maple Avenue and Oak Street.)

maintenance   N. the act of keeping something in good working order (Changing the oil regularly is part of careful car *maintenance*.)

optional   ADJ. a matter of choice (Leather upholstery is *optional* with the car, so you can decide whether or not you want it.)

overhaul   V. to take apart and make changes or repairs (After you *overhaul* the engine, it should be almost as good as new.)

pedestrian   N. a person traveling on foot (If a *pedestrian* is crossing the street, the driver should stop and let him or her walk to the other side.)

recoup   V. win or earn back losses (We can *recoup* the money we spent on the car by selling it.)

retractable   ADJ. able to be drawn back in (Just after take off, the *retractable* landing gear was pulled up into the body of the plane.)

security   N. the condition of being free from danger (The passengers had a feeling of *security* because Joe was such a careful driver.)

stipend   N. allowance or money paid (The company gave employees a gas *stipend* to cover traveling expenses.)

toboggan   N. a narrow, runnerless sled (Our three-person *toboggan* shot down the runs at blinding speeds.)

transmission   N. the mechanism in an automobile that controls the gears (When the *transmission* was broken, he could not shift from one gear to another.)

unscathed   ADJ. not hurt; not marked (Because she was wearing a seat belt, she escaped injury and walked away from the accident *unscathed*.)

Exercise 1
Write the letter of the word set that best completes the sentence.

1. Proper automobile _____ includes putting _____ in the radiator in the fall.   _____
   A. coupe — asphalt
   B. horsepower — intersection
   C. security — stipend
   D. maintenance — antifreeze

2. A _____ should always look both ways when crossing a busy _____. _____
   A. stipend — toboggan
   B. pedestrian — intersection
   C. dashboard — coupe
   D. intersection — horsepower

3. The five-speed _____ is a(n) _____ feature on this model car. _____
   A. security — retractable
   B. toboggan — unscathed
   C. transmission — optional
   D. asphalt — optional

4. On the _____ of the two-door _____ you will find the oil gauge. _____
   A. dashboard — coupe
   B. horsepower — security
   C. security — intersection
   D. toboggan — stipend

5. Having enough _____ to pass safely on the highway, gives the driver a feeling of _____

   _____.
   A. pedestrian — stipend
   B. horsepower — security
   C. intersection — transmission
   D. coupe — asphalt

6. The team on the _____ was _____ in the accident. _____
   A. antifreeze — optional
   B. dashboard — retractable
   C. asphalt — unscathed
   D. toboggan — unscathed

7. They will _____ fuel if they take the _____ highway rather than the gravel road. _____
   A. conserve — asphalt
   B. inflate — asphalt
   C. exceed — coupe
   D. overhaul — stipend

8. Because it was not working properly, the mechanics decided to _____ the plane's _____
   _____ landing gear.
   A. recoup — optional
   B. transport — unscathed
   C. overhaul — retractable
   D. exceed — optional

9. He paid the man to _____ the tires out of the _____ he'd been given for car repair. _____
   A. inflate — stipend
   B. recoup — exceed
   C. overhaul — pedestrian
   D. transport — overhaul

10. If we _____ the price we agreed on, we'll never _____ the money later. _____
   A. overhaul — transport
   B. exceed — recoup
   C. inflate — exceed
   D. recoup — transport

Exercise 2

Write the letter of the word that most nearly has the *opposite* meaning of the italicized word.

11. *optional*	A. voluntary	B. required	C. free	D. unable	_____
12. *retractable*	A. counted	B. fine	C. single	D. extendable	_____
13. *recoup*	A. lose	B. trust	C. handle	D. hide	_____
14. *unscathed*	A. alone	B. taken	C. asleep	D. harmed	_____
15. *security*	A. safety	B. danger	C. peace	D. protection	_____
16. *inflate*	A. enforce	B. correct	C. break	D. deflate	_____
17. *exceed*	A. take up	B. fall short	C. put out	D. part with	_____
18. *pedestrian*	A. jogger	B. policeman	C. rider	D. mayor	_____
19. *overhaul*	A. examine	B. destroy	C. weigh	D. count	_____
20. *conserve*	A. carry	B. waste	C. move	D. drive	_____

Lesson 19
Suffixes — -ation/-tion/-ion/-sion

All the words in this lesson contain the suffixes -ation, -tion, -ion, or -sion, denoting "the act, state, quality, or condition."

consumption   N. the act of using up (The city's *consumption* of water increases during the hot summer months.)

contention   N. controversy; dispute (There is some *contention* between the two brothers about who will get the extra dessert.)

deceleration   N. the act of decreasing speed (When he jammed on the brake, there was rapid *deceleration* of the race car.)

deception   N. the act of misleading (He resorted to *deception* when he used a fake name.)

deprivation   N. the state of being without; loss (The college student experienced sleep *deprivation* during final exam week.)

emigration   N. leaving one's own country or region to settle in another (Aiko told about her family's *emigration* from Japan to the United States.)

expectation   N. looking forward to or believing that something will happen (We ordered extra food with the *expectation* that we might have uninvited guests.)

exploitation   N. the act of making the greatest possible use of (Labor unions fight against the *exploitation* of factory workers.)

ingestion   N. the act of taking in food (Grandpa insists that a daily *ingestion* of yogurt keeps you healthy.)

innovation   N. a new creation or change (The *innovation* of the sewing machine was welcomed by women who had always before sewn by hand.)

isolation   N. the condition of being separated from other people (The famous writer lives in *isolation* on a remote island.)

moderation   N. freedom from excess (Eating in *moderation* will prevent weight gain.)

modification   N. a change (A slight *modification* in the building plans will result in an extra window.)

nomination   N. a naming, as a candidate for office (The President's *nomination* of a cabinet member must be approved by the Senate.)

perception   N. the act of understanding (Since we disagree about politics, my brother's *perception* of world affairs is different from mine.)

preoccupation   N. the act of being absorbed in thought (Because of her *preoccupation* with basketball, Juanita cannot concentrate on her homework.)

prescription   N. a written direction from a doctor for preparing and using medicine (After reading the *prescription,* the druggist prepared the medicine for the patient.)

profusion   N. great quantity or amount (A *profusion* of tennis shoes, balls, T-shirts, and sweat pants littered Carla's bedroom.)

promotion   N. an advance in rank or importance (A higher salary and more responsibility came with Ramon's *promotion.*)

sanitation   N. the measures taken to protect public health (The disposal of garbage is a major *sanitation* problem in many large cities.)

Exercise 1
Write the letter of the word that best completes the sentence.

1. According to recent surveys, the _____ of chicken has increased over the last ten years.   _____
   A. emigration   B. nomination   C. consumption   D. ignition

2. The farmer cared for the healthy seedlings with the _____ of a good harvest.   _____
   A. ignition   B. ingestion   C. expectation   D. nomination

3. John and his family enjoyed the _____ of their weekend cabin in the woods.
   A. prescription   B. deprivation   C. ingestion   D. isolation   _____

4. In spring, there is a _____ of blossoms on cherry trees.
   A. moderation   B. profusion   C. sanitation   D. deceleration   _____

5. To prevent sore muscles, you should practice _____ in exercising.
   A. nomination   B. moderation   C. ingestion   D. expectation   _____

6. The train's rapid _____ caused its cargo to shift.
   A. deceleration   B. perception   C. prescription   D. deprivation   _____

7. Joe's _____ for treasurer was greeted with enthusiasm.
   A. isolation   B. emigration   C. sanitation   D. nomination   _____

8. The _____ of Irish to the United States in the 1840's was due to a famine in Ireland.
   A. consumption   B. ignition   C. emigration   D. sanitation   _____

9. A _____ of the dress pattern will make the costume fit better.
   A. prescription   B. contention   C. sanitation   D. modification   _____

10. The _____ of natural resources has led to an interest in recycling.
    A. emigration   B. exploitation   C. profusion   D. nomination   _____

11. Susie's _____ with animals indicates that she may become a veterinarian.
    A. deception   B. deceleration   C. moderation   D. preoccupation   _____

12. He is enthusiastic about almost any _____ just because it is new.
    A. ingestion   B. innovation   C. deceleration   D. isolation   _____

13. The doctor's handwriting on the _____ was difficult for the pharmacist to read.
    A. prescription   B. preoccupation   C. contention   D. ignition   _____

14. The _____ of a poisonous substance can cause death.
    A. nomination   B. ingestion   C. emigration   D. isolation   _____

15. The _____ between the two leaders has prevented the treaty.
    A. ingestion   B. deprivation   C. sanitation   D. contention   _____

Exercise 2

Write the letter of the word pair that has a relationship similar to the relationship of the first word pair.

16. **sanitation : disease : :**   A. happiness : joy   C. shoe : foot   _____
         B. caution : accidents   D. oak : tree

17. **deception : deceive : :**   A. election : elect   C. hide : hidden   _____
         B. rainbow : rain   D. sadness : sad

18. **perception : insight : :**   A. forgive : blame   C. tall : high   _____
         B. loud : soft   D. motion : stillness

19. **promotion : job : :**   A. art : painting   C. dime : nickel   _____
         B. cavern : cave   D. raise : salary

20. **deprivation : prosperity : :**   A. ancient : modern   C. paint : brush   _____
         B. parade : march   D. toe : foot

Lesson 20
Agriculture

All the words in this lesson may be associated with agriculture.

arable   ADJ. appropriate for plowing (The land was no longer *arable* after the toxic chemicals had seeped through the ground.)

heifer   N. a young cow (When the *heifer* is grown, it will be a fine dairy cow.)

incubator   N. container used to warm and hatch eggs (Keep the temperature in the *incubator* from changing if you want the eggs to hatch.)

irrigate   V. to water by means of ditches or pipes (The Egyptians used water from the Nile to *irrigate* their fields.)

operative   ADJ. in operation; working (The tractor has been repaired and is now *operative*.)

pasteurize   V. to destroy bacteria in some liquids through a process of heating and cooling (If you *pasteurize* milk, it will not carry bacterial diseases.)

precipitation   N. the depositing of rain or snow from the atmosphere (We have had a dry spring, so the farmers are hoping for *precipitation* in the summer.)

prepay   V. to pay for in advance (If you *prepay* the bill for the seeds, you will not have to write a check when they arrive.)

probable   ADJ. likely to happen or be true (The *probable* result of fertilizing is a bigger crop.)

prosperous   ADJ. making money; doing well (The *prosperous* farmer had a large farm and always sold his crops for a good profit.)

rampant   ADJ. spreading without restraint (Weeds ran *rampant* over the untended field.)

ravage   V. ruin or destroy (If there are no birds to eat insects, the insects will *ravage* the crops.)

raven   N. a large, black crow (The dark shape of a *raven* circled high above the field.)

sample   V. to try out (The buyer will *sample* the home-grown vegetables before placing a large order.)

severity   N. harshness (Many crops were damaged because of the *severity* of the hail storm.)

shuck   V. to remove the outer covering of a thing (We will *shuck* the corn and give the husks to the horses.)

toil   V. to work hard (To weed the entire field, they will have to *toil* in the hot sun all day.)

tract   N. a large area (There were three acres in the *tract* of land the farmer sold to his neighbor.)

transplant   V. to move from one place to another (We can dig up these bushes and *transplant* them on the other side of the house.)

yoke   N. a wooden bar used to hold animals together as they pull something (The boy put the *yoke* on the two oxen so they could pull the plow.)

Exercise 1
Write the letter of the word that best completes the sentence.

1. Before you leave the farm, you should _____ the apple cider.
   A. transplant   B. toil   C. ravage   D. sample   _____

2. We grow corn on the _____ of land near the highway.
   A. tract   B. precipitation   C. heifer   D. severity   _____

3. The glossy black feathers of the _____ shone as it perched on a branch.
   A. incubator   B. heifer   C. raven   D. yoke   _____

4. To _____ the fifty ears of corn will take nearly an hour.   _____
   A. pasteurize   B. ravage   C. sample   D. shuck

5. After we _____ the milk, we cool it in the refrigerator.   _____
   A. pasteurize   B. transplant   C. shuck   D. toil

6. Even though there are dark clouds in the sky, no _____ is forecast.   _____
   A. severity   B. tract   C. precipitation   D. raven

7. The _____ land of the midwestern plains was well suited to growing of corn and   _____
   grain.
   A. operative   B. arable   C. rampant   D. probable

8. Please help me _____ the tree from the front yard to the back yard.   _____
   A. toil   B. shuck   C. ravage   D. transplant

9. When it is six months old, the _____ can be separated from its mother.   _____
   A. raven   B. heifer   C. incubator   D. yoke

10. Be sure the _____ is fastened securely to the two plow horses.   _____
    A. raven   B. incubator   C. yoke   D. heifer

Exercise 2

Write the letter of the word that most nearly has the *opposite* meaning of the italicized
word.

11. *rampant*	A. terrible	B. sheepish	C. controlled	D. alone	_____
12. *incubator*	A. cooler	B. nest	C. basket	D. hospital	_____
13. *operative*	A. oiled	B. heavy	C. broken	D. foreign	_____
14. *prosperous*	A. poor	B. tall	C. careful	D. damp	_____
15. *irrigate*	A. dry	B. divide	C. block	D. open	_____
16. *toil*	A. hoe	B. play	C. wrap	D. eat	_____
17. *severity*	A. humor	B. cold	C. gentleness	D. temperature	_____
18. *prepay*	A. charge	B. insist	C. order	D. grab	_____
19. *probable*	A. reasonable	B. sad	C. taken	D. unlikely	_____
20. *ravage*	A. tend	B. spend	C. plow	D. drink	_____

Lesson 21
The Military

All the words in this lesson may be associated with the military.

assail   V. to attack (When they *assail* the fortress, they will use a cannon to open a hole in the wall.)

barricade   V. to obstruct with a barrier (If the students *barricade* the street with the trash cans, no cars will be able to get through.)

bravery   N. fearlessness (She showed *bravery* in battle by risking her life to aid a fallen comrade.)

bungle   V. to spoil through clumsy behavior (The soldiers were afraid that the insensitive general would *bungle* the peace talks.)

caliber   N. quality (The high *caliber* of the troops was due to their excellent training.)

civilian   ADJ. not having to do with the armed forces (His *civilian* clothes felt strange after such a long time in uniform.)

court-martial   N. a trial by a military court (At the *court-martial* the sailor was accused of disobeying his captain.)

cunning   ADJ. sly; cleverly deceptive (Hiding soldiers inside the Trojan Horse so they would be pulled into the city was a *cunning* plan.)

decoy   N. any person or thing used to lure another into a trap (A small band of cavalry acted as a *decoy* to draw the Confederate army out onto the plain where they would be defenseless.)

deploy   V. to spread troops out over an area (The general will *deploy* his armies along a five-mile stretch of the river.)

disband   V. to break up (As soon as the war is over, we will *disband* the troops.)

discharge   V. to fire or shoot (There will be a loud noise when they *discharge* the cannon.)

dispatch   N. a written message (The runner carried the *dispatch* from the field commander to headquarters.)

fortify   V. to strengthen; give support to (*Fortify* the south gate in case there is an attack from that direction.)

fortress   N. a large protected and secure place (Inside the enemy *fortress* was a command post and a small town.)

impregnable   ADJ. not able to be overcome by force (None of the enemy was able to break through the walls of the *impregnable* castle at the top of the cliff.)

mobilize   V. to call into action (If war is declared, the king will *mobilize* his armies and send them off to fight.)

opposition   N. resistance or hostility (There was strong *opposition* to the suggestion that troops should be sent to fight a losing battle.)

sentry   N. a person assigned to guard or protect a group (At night, a *sentry* was posted at the gate.)

strategic   ADJ. important or essential in relation to a plan (The retreat of the troops was a *strategic* maneuver designed to fool the enemy.)

Exercise 1
Write the letter of the word that best completes the sentence.

1. When they _____ the army, the soldiers can return home.
   A. assail   B. disband   C. bungle   D. mobilize   _____

2. If you handle a loaded gun, there is a danger that it will _____ accidentally.
   A. fortify   B. disband   C. mobilize   D. discharge   _____

3. The cavalry planned to _____ the enemy camp after dark.   _____
   A. deploy   B. discharge   C. assail   D. mobilize

4. He was sent as a(n) _____ to lead the attackers into a trap.   _____
   A. dispatch   B. decoy   C. opposition   D. fortress

5. Inside the _____ fort, he was safe from the enemy.   _____
   A. impregnable   B. cunning   C. strategic   D. civilian

6. The ancient _____ has protected the town for hundreds of years.   _____
   A. decoy   B. opposition   C. bravery   D. fortress

7. If we don't _____ the wall, the enemy will break through.   _____
   A. discharge   B. fortify   C. deploy   D. mobilize

8. Troops of such high _____ are rare.   _____
   A. fortress   B. decoy   C. caliber   D. sentry

9. Our _____ foe tricked us into betraying our position.   _____
   A. cunning   B. impregnable   C. civilian   D. strategic

10. The commander used a carrier pigeon to send a(n) _____ to the general.   _____
    A. opposition   B. decoy   C. caliber   D. dispatch

11. All soldiers should report to their regiments if the emperor decides to _____ the   _____
    army.
    A. discharge   B. mobilize   C. disband   D. assail

12. There was loud _____ to our plan of attack because no one thought it would work.   _____
    A. fortress   B. sentry   C. dispatch   D. opposition

13. The enemy will be ready for us if you _____ the surprise attack.   _____
    A. mobilize   B. bungle   C. assail   D. disband

14. Army lawyers prepared for the _____ of the private.   _____
    A. opposition   B. sentry   C. bravery   D. court-martial

15. If we _____ all our troops in the south, the north will be undefended.   _____
    A. deploy   B. disband   C. discharge   D. assail

Exercise 2

Write the letter of the word pair that has a relationship similar to the relationship of the
first word pair.

16. *strategic : strategy : :*   A. singing : song   C. beautiful : beauty   _____
                                    B. man : woman   D. hang : hung

17. *barricade : prevent : :*   A. roof : house   C. open : allow   _____
                                    B. brush : paint   D. up : down

18. *civilian : military : :*   A. wet : dry   C. small : little   _____
                                    B. city : building   D. train : whistle

19. *sentry : guard : :*   A. helmet : head   C. queen : prince   _____
                                    B. palomino : horse   D. tree : branch

20. *bravery : danger : :*   A. ring : finger   C. generosity : need   _____
                                    B. talk : voice   D. friend : enemy

Lesson 22
Headline News

All the words in this lesson may be associated with headlines in the news.

armistice   N. a temporary stop in fighting (During the *armistice,* the soldiers laid down their arms while the leaders talked about peace.)

ban   V. to prohibit by law (Because the city plans to *ban* fireworks, we won't set off sparklers this year.)

brawl   V. to quarrel or fight noisily (The teams began to *brawl* after the tense game.)

controversial   ADJ. subject to argument or debate (Nuclear power is a *controversial* issue because there are strong feelings both for and against it.)

dispel   V. to drive away or cause to disappear (Plans for the new playground will *dispel* fears that the city has forgotten about its parks.)

drought   N. a continued period with little or no rain (During the six weeks of the *drought,* not a drop of water fell.)

endless   ADJ. never stopping; having no end (After what seemed like *endless* delays, the space shuttle finally took off.)

epidemic   N. the rapid spread of a disease (The *epidemic* of measles has closed the city's schools.)

foretell   V. to predict; to tell beforehand (A woman claims her special powers allow her to *foretell* the future of our planet.)

immigration   N. the state of entering and living in a foreign country (*Immigration* laws limit the number of foreign people who may move to the United States each year.)

innovation   N. something newly introduced (Microwave ovens are a recent *innovation.*)

invasion   N. the act of attacking or taking over (An *invasion* of thousands of fruit flies threatened the peach crop.)

irreparable   ADJ. not able to be made good or repaired (Because the bomb caused *irreparable* damage, the building will have to be torn down.)

participate   V. to take part (Representatives from every city in the state will *participate* in a discussion on pollution.)

racial   ADJ. having to do with race or common origin (The city is proud of the *racial* harmony that exists among its citizens of many different cultures.)

rebellion   N. an armed fight against one's government (During the *rebellion,* the palace was attacked by those who opposed the king's policies.)

significance   N. importance (The *significance* of the new fertilizer is that twice as much corn can now be grown on an acre.)

summit   N. the highest point of a mountain (When the climbers reached the *summit,* they planted their country's flag on the mountaintop.)

survivor   N. one who remains safe through a dangerous situation that has taken the lives of others (Only one *survivor* lived to tell the story of the airplane crash.)

unbiased   ADJ. with an open mind; without prejudice (The newspaper's *unbiased* report listed the good and bad points of each candidate.)

Exercise 1
Write the letter of the word that best completes the sentence.

1. The _____ of many nationalities has given America its unique flavor.
   A. survivor   B. immigration   C. summit   D. significance   _____

2. No one could _____ who would win the war.
   A. foretell   B. ban   C. brawl   D. participate   _____

3. Signing the _____ brought a halt to the fighting in the four-year border dispute.
   A. drought   B. epidemic   C. armistice   D. significance   _____

4. Many _____ and ethnic groups live side-by-side in our city.   _____
   A. racial   B. irreparable   C. endless   D. unbiased

5. Although the newspaper claims that the damage to the theater is _____, the   _____
   owners have ordered repairs to begin immediately.
   A. irreparable   B. unbiased   C. racial   D. controversial

6. To _____ rumors of a plant closing, the manager announced that additional   _____
   employees would be hired.
   A. brawl   B. participate   C. ban   D. dispel

7. The _____ of the fire suffered third degree burns.   _____
   A. invasion   B. survivor   C. drought   D. armistice

8. The press secretary will _____ all reporters from the meeting.   _____
   A. ban   B. brawl   C. foretell   D. participate

9. During the flu _____, over half of the office staff was absent from work.   _____
   A. rebellion   B. drought   C. armistice   D. epidemic

10. The farmers could not protect their fields from the unexpected _____ of locusts.   _____
    A. drought   B. summit   C. invasion   D. armistice

11. Since the angry fans may _____ after the game, security guards are stationed   _____
    throughout the stadium.
    A. ban   B. brawl   C. foretell   D. dispel

12. The army planned a(n) _____ against the government in power.   _____
    A. immigration   B. survivor   C. rebellion   D. drought

13. The world was shocked by the country's refusal to _____ in the Olympic Games.   _____
    A. ban   B. participate   C. foretell   D. dispel

14. The _____ of the meeting is indicated by the number of reporters outside the door.   _____
    A. drought   B. survivor   C. significance   D. epidemic

15. A new hand-held device that measures blood pressure is a(n) _____ in home   _____
    health care.
    A. epidemic   B. invasion   C. rebellion   D. innovation

Exercise 2

Write the letter of the word pair that has a relationship similar to the relationship of the
first word pair.

16. **controversial : issue : :**   A. argument : debate   C. jacket : coat   _____
                                      B. funny : movie   D. think : problem

17. **drought : flood : :**   A. ring : finger   C. truth : idea   _____
                                      B. mistake : error   D. famine : feast

18. **summit : base : :**   A. grass : mower   C. high : low   _____
                                      B. disease : sickness   D. cloud : rain

19. **unbiased : fair : :**   A. old : new   C. believable : ugly   _____
                                      B. cool : chilly   D. reporter : newspaper

20. **endless : everlasting : :**   A. beautiful : beauty   C. end : finish   _____
                                      B. joyful : joy   D. carefree : lighthearted

Lesson 23
Performing Arts

All the words in this lesson may be associated with the performing arts.

acoustics   N. that which affects sound in a room (The fine *acoustics* in the concert hall made it possible to hear every note.)

animation   N. liveliness (Whirling around the stage, the dancers performed the dance with spirit and *animation*.)

aria   N. a song in an opera sung by one person (The leading lady began to sing the *aria* after the other cast members had left the stage.)

baritone   N. the male singing voice that is higher than bass and lower than tenor, or a person having such a voice (The mellow voice of the *baritone* could be heard singing German love songs.)

cameo   N. a small role in a play or movie done by a well-known actor or actress (As a favor to the producer, the movie star promised to make a *cameo* appearance in the picture.)

chorus   N. any group of singers, speakers, or dancers who perform songs, words, or dances together as a group (There were twenty dancers in the *chorus* of the musical.)

conservatory   N. a school of music (She studied music at the *conservatory* for many years before starting her professional career.)

diva   N. the leading lady in an opera (The *diva* was asked to sing in operas throughout the world.)

dramatist   N. someone who writes plays (The great *dramatist* was a master at writing dialogue.)

favorable   ADJ. in favor of; encouraging (The critic praised the play in her *favorable* review.)

flair   N. a natural talent (He was rarely asked to do comedy because he had such a *flair* for dramatic roles.)

intermission   N. a break; a pause in activity (There will be a short *intermission* between the first and second acts of the play.)

melodrama   N. a story or play with exaggerated events designed to stir up emotions (The audience was moved to tears by the tragic events in the *melodrama*.)

premiere   N. the first performance of a play or movie (The public will see the movie for the first time at the *premiere* on Friday night.)

production   N. a showing of a play (The actor was ill and could not appear in last night's *production* of Hamlet.)

projector   N. a machine used to cause an image to be visible on a screen (As the lights went down, the *projector* was turned on, and the movie began.)

repertory   N. a list of pieces a group or a person can perform (The singer's *repertory* included rock music and country ballads.)

tenor   N. the highest male singing voice, or a person having such a voice (The notes are high, so we need a *tenor* for this song.)

theatrical   ADJ. having to do with the theater (Throughout her long career as an actress, she has loved the *theatrical* life.)

troupe   N. a group of actors or other performers (Every year, we look forward to the arrival of the *troupe* that runs the summer theater.)

Exercise 1
Write the letter of the word pair that best completes the sentence.

1. The _____ was pleased with the _____ reaction to her new play. _____
   A. projector — cameo   C. dramatist — favorable
   B. troupe — favorable   D. aria — theatrical

2. We all want to attend the _____ of his new _____ next week.   _____
   A. melodrama — tenor
   B. premiere — production
   C. repertory — animation
   D. baritone — acceptance

3. When the _____ broke, a short _____ was announced to allow time to repair it.   _____
   A. projector — intermission
   B. aria — diva
   C. premiere — melodrama
   D. dramatist — flair

4. Listening to the _____ sing the _____ was an experience I'll never forget.   _____
   A. animation — baritone
   B. flair — conservatory
   C. chorus — flair
   D. diva — aria

5. We need a man with a voice higher than a _____, but we can't find a _____ .   _____
   A. aria — chorus
   B. production — repertory
   C. baritone — tenor
   D. melodrama — troupe

6. The members of the _____ are _____ people who love putting on Shakespeare's   _____
   plays.
   A. aria — cameo
   B. troupe — theatrical
   C. flair — theatrical
   D. dramatist — favorable

7. The _____ of the _____ included both popular music and classical music.   _____
   A. repertory — chorus
   B. baritone — animation
   C. diva — dramatist
   D. repertory — flair

8. The actress has a _____ for the type of _____ common on soap operas.   _____
   A. premiere — production
   B. repertory — tenor
   C. intermission — troupe
   D. flair — melodrama

9. The poor _____ in the auditorium of the _____ made it difficult to hear student   _____
   performances.
   A. diva — aria
   B. flair — chorus
   C. acoustics — conservatory
   D. production — projector

10. She made only a _____ appearance, but her performance was filled with _____.   _____
    A. cameo — animation
    B. favorable — flair
    C. theatrical — acceptance
    D. favorable — baritone

Exercise 2

Write the letter of the word that most nearly has the *same* meaning of the italicized
word.

11. *intermission*	A. end	B. endurance	C. recess	D. persistence	_____
12. *premiere*	A. opening	B. actor	C. closing	D. play	_____
13. *favorable*	A. contrary	B. unfavorable	C. good	D. adverse	_____
14. *flair*	A. inadequacy	B. ability	C. idleness	D. hunger	_____
15. *troupe*	A. growth	B. trumpet	C. singer	D. company	_____
16. *dramatist*	A. dancer	B. performer	C. playwright	D. actor	_____
17. *aria*	A. trapeze	B. actress	C. curtain	D. song	_____
18. *conservatory*	A. school	B. office	C. stage	D. planetarium	_____
19. *animation*	A. sleepiness	B. activity	C. bravery	D. humor	_____
20. *diva*	A. actress	B. dancer	C. singer	D. pianist	_____

Lesson 24
The Home

All the words in this lesson may be associated with the home.

candelabrum   N. a large candleholder with several arms (Grandmother's *candelabrum* holds six candles.)

doily   N. a decorative mat often made of lace (The lace *doily* under the vase is a pretty way to protect the table top.)

domestic   ADJ. having to do with the home (Washing dishes and making beds are *domestic* chores.)

douse   V. to put out (Use baking soda or salt to *douse* a grease fire.)

embroider   V. to decorate with needlework designs (He used red yarn to *embroider* his initials on the swimming towel.)

floral   ADJ. having to do with flowers (Large pink and white daisies were in the *floral* pattern of the couch.)

gadget   N. a clever device (This *gadget* will peel potatoes.)

gilt   ADJ. having a thin layer of gold placed on the surface for decoration (The *gilt* picture frame shone in the candlelight.)

grille   N. a decorative grating, screen, or door (The iron *grille* outside the window was attractive and kept intruders from getting in.)

habitable   ADJ. able to be lived in (The house was *habitable,* but the occupants were often cold because there was no heat.)

ignite   V. to set on fire (Use this match to *ignite* the fire.)

incense   N. a sweet smelling substance that is usually burned (The smoke from the *incense* filled the room with a pleasant odor.)

lavatory   N. a room with facilities for washing, usually including a toilet (Clean the *lavatory* after you finish shaving.)

midday   ADJ. having to do with the middle of the day (Our *midday* meal was served promptly at noon.)

misplace   V. to put in the wrong place (You will not *misplace* your keys if you always hang them on this nail.)

ottoman   N. footstool (Put your feet up on the *ottoman* and relax.)

porcelain   N. a fine ceramic that is white and translucent (You almost see through the sides of a delicate teacup made of *porcelain*.)

removal   N. a taking away (*Removal* of the tree left a big hole in the ground.)

spigot   N. valve used to control the flow of water or other liquids (He turned the *spigot,* and water gushed from the hose.)

upholster   V. to cover furniture with fabric (If we *upholster* the chair in red corduroy, it will match the crimson pillows on the sofa.)

Exercise 1

Write the letters of the words that best complete the sentence.

1. She was not a _____ person because she hated doing things around the house.   _____
   A. floral   B. domestic   C. midday   D. habitable

2. Her pale, smooth skin looked almost like _____.   _____
   A. doily   B. grille   C. ottoman   D. porcelain

3. At the hardware store he bought an electronic _____ that would beep when anyone tried to open the garage door.   _____
   A. gadget   B. porcelain   C. incense   D. removal

4. The _____ arrangement on the table included daffodils and tulips.   _____
   A. habitable   B. floral   C. gilt   D. midday

5. The candles in the _____ provided enough light for dining. _____
   A. doily   B. lavatory   C. ottoman   D. candelabrum

6. Since children play on the sofa, we should _____ it with a strong fabric. _____
   A. ignite   B. misplace   C. upholster   D. douse

7. Grandmother put a _____ over the back of the chair to keep it clean. _____
   A. lavatory   B. doily   C. porcelain   D. spigot

8. The _____ of old boxes from the basement will give us more space. _____
   A. removal   B. candelabrum   C. incense   D. lavatory

9. Burning _____ in your room could be a fire hazard. _____
   A. ottoman   B. incense   C. gadget   D. doily

10. To minimize fire danger, they were careful to _____ the coals in the barbecue grill _____
    before going inside.
    A. misplace   B. embroider   C. douse   D. ignite

Exercise 2

Write the letter of the word that most nearly has the *same* meaning as the italicized word.

11. *spigot*	A. glass	B. tub	C. faucet	D. hose	_____
12. *misplace*	A. find	B. lose	C. discard	D. retrieve	_____
13. *midday*	A. noon	B. midnight	C. morning	D. evening	_____
14. *lavatory*	A. closet	B. bedroom	C. kitchen	D. bathroom	_____
15. *ignite*	A. light	B. soak	C. heat	D. drench	_____
16. *embroider*	A. sketch	B. stretch	C. paint	D. sew	_____
17. *gilt*	A. conscious	B. golden	C. blue	D. old	_____
18. *grille*	A. pit	B. curtain	C. roast	D. grate	_____
19. *habitable*	A. livable	B. beautiful	C. dirty	D. unusual	_____
20. *ottoman*	A. chair	B. table	C. stool	D. bed	_____

Lesson 25
Suffixes — -ful/-ous

All the words in this lesson contain the suffixes *-ful* and *-ous* which mean "full of."

atrocious   ADJ. cruel or wicked (Whipping the dog that was tied to the fence was an *atrocious* act.)

continuous   ADJ. without a stop or break (No intermissions interrupted the *continuous* music at the outdoor concert.)

delightful   ADJ. enjoyable (We spent a *delightful* afternoon hiking by the lake.)

disastrous   ADJ. causing destruction, suffering, or loss (The *disastrous* tornado leveled every building in its path.)

doubtful   ADJ. without certainty (We are *doubtful* about tomorrow's picnic, since rain is predicted.)

extraneous   ADJ. not needed; not bearing upon or related to the matter at hand (You should take out the *extraneous* information in your essay and only include facts about the topic.)

grateful   ADJ. appreciative for kindness or benefits received (The foreign exchange student will always be *grateful* for the kindness of her host family.)

hilarious   ADJ. extremely funny (People doubled over with laughter when they heard Jolene's *hilarious* stories.)

mountainous   ADJ. like a mountain; enormous (During the storm, the *mountainous* waves made the sailboat seem tiny.)

obnoxious   ADJ. extremely annoying or unpleasant (At the dinner party, the *obnoxious* young man talked loudly and interrupted other conversations.)

prestigious   ADJ. having a reputation, influence, or distinction based on prior achievements (The *prestigious* law firm is known throughout the state for its excellent work.)

remorseful   ADJ. feeling or showing deep regret for having done wrong (The *remorseful* child wept as she told how sorry she was that she had broken the dish.)

resentful   ADJ. feeling or showing bitterness over a real or imagined insult or offense (Cheryl felt *resentful* when she was not chosen to play for the concert, since her best friend had been selected.)

slanderous   ADJ. containing or involving false information that could damage the reputation of another (Even though the *slanderous* statement that John had taken drugs was untrue, it ruined his chances of becoming class president.)

strenuous   ADJ. requiring great effort or energy (After today's *strenuous* practice, the whole team was exhausted.)

superstitious   ADJ. having faith in magic or chance (Because he is *superstitious,* he thinks that breaking a mirror will bring seven years of bad luck.)

tenacious   ADJ. holding firmly; stubborn (Julio tried to pry the plastic ball from the *tenacious* jaws of his puppy.)

unscrupulous   ADJ. not honorable; without conscience (Paying herself a large salary out of the company funds was an *unscrupulous* practice.)

vigorous   ADJ. full of energy; lively (Instead of walking, he prefers the more *vigorous* exercise of bicycle riding.)

wishful   ADJ. having or expressing a wish (The *wishful* look on the child's face revealed her desire for the doll in the window.)

Exercise 1
Write the letter of the word that best completes the sentence.

1. Her _____ eyes begged for forgiveness.

    A. extraneous   B. remorseful   C. strenuous   D. mountainous

2. The _____ train wreck claimed the lives of three hundred people.
   A. wishful   B. hilarious   C. continuous   D. disastrous

3. Lorraine seems hurt and _____ when her baby sister is the center of attention.
   A. delightful   B. resentful   C. extraneous   D. prestigious

4. An extremely _____ person might refuse to get out of bed on Friday the 13th.
   A. mountainous   B. continuous   C. grateful   D. superstitious

5. Daydreaming and _____ thinking took up most of the unhappy girl's time.
   A. prestigious   B. wishful   C. disastrous   D. mountainous

6. Few readers believed the magazine's _____ remarks, so the actor's reputation remained spotless.
   A. strenuous   B. mountainous   C. slanderous   D. grateful

7. With a _____ effort, we managed to reach the top of the mountain before dark.
   A. vigorous   B. superstitious   C. remorseful   D. slanderous

8. It was difficult to see the main point of his story since there were so many _____ details.
   A. grateful   B. prestigious   C. extraneous   D. mountainous

9. The main character is a(n) _____ woman who will stop at nothing to become rich and famous.
   A. continuous   B. mountainous   C. grateful   D. unscrupulous

10. As the climber hung in midair, her _____ grip on the rope was the only thing that saved her.
    A. tenacious   B. superstitious   C. hilarious   D. slanderous

Exercise 2

Write the letter of the word that most nearly has the *opposite* meaning of the italicized word.

11. **strenuous**   A. ignorant   B. difficult   C. easy   D. muscular
12. **mountainous**   A. small   B. exciting   C. gigantic   D. rough
13. **continuous**   A. fragrant   B. dangerous   C. long   D. interrupted
14. **doubtful**   A. sure   B. unhappy   C. colorful   D. patient
15. **atrocious**   A. starry   B. good   C. heavy   D. willing
16. **prestigious**   A. crooked   B. unimportant   C. rich   D. beautiful
17. **delightful**   A. easy   B. thoughtful   C. funny   D. unpleasant
18. **obnoxious**   A. enjoyable   B. irritating   C. bothersome   D. mysterious
19. **hilarious**   A. amazing   B. humorless   C. high   D. complicated
20. **grateful**   A. happy   B. intelligent   C. thankless   D. delicate

Lesson 26
Occupations

All of the words in this lesson may be associated with occupations.

administrator   N. a manager; an executive (The *administrator* called a meeting of his employees.)

applicant   N. someone who applies for something such as a job, a loan, or admission to a school (Each *applicant* gave reasons why he or she wanted the job.)

apprenticeship   N. working for another in order to learn a trade or a skill (After two years, Mario had completed his *apprenticeship* to the master builder and was ready to work on his own as a carpenter.)

aviator   N. a pilot; one who flies airplanes (Charles Lindbergh was the first *aviator* to make a solo, non-stop flight across the Atlantic.)

bacteriologist   N. a scientist who studies one-celled organisms or plants (The *bacteriologist* gave a lecture on plant diseases caused by bacteria.)

biochemist   N. a scientist who studies the chemical process of living matter (The *biochemist* spoke about the ways chemicals in the body affect personality.)

brigadier   N. a brigadier general; a commissioned officer in the armed services (A *brigadier* is ranked higher than a colonel, but lower than a major general.)

broker   N. someone who buys and sells things for others such as stocks, bonds, or real estate (A real estate *broker* helped us sell our house.)

chaplain   N. priest, minister, or rabbi assigned to conduct religious services for the military or other institution (The *chaplain* led the soldiers in prayer.)

corporal   N. noncommissioned service officer (A *corporal* ranks higher than a private, but lower than a sergeant.)

darkroom   N. a room used to develop photographs (Only special light is allowed in the *darkroom* while photographs are being developed.)

dispatcher   N. one who sends out vehicles according to a schedule (The *dispatcher* must know the locations of all the buses to keep them running on time.)

efficiency   N. ability to work with the least amount of wasted time, effort, or money (If the engineers can improve the *efficiency* of the engine, the car will use less gas.)

engraver   N. a person who carves or cuts designs into solid objects (The *engraver* carved my name on the bracelet.)

executive   N. a director of a business (An *executive* of the company made the decision to change the product's design.)

mason   N. a skilled craftsman who works with stone, brick, or concrete (A *mason* was hired to build the new stone wall.)

usher   N. a person who shows others to their seats in places such as churches and theaters (The *usher* looked at our tickets to find the seat numbers.)

vocation   N. profession or occupation (She chose teaching as a *vocation* because she enjoyed teenagers.)

warden   N. person in charge of a prison (The *warden* was responsible for the welfare of the prisoners.)

wholesaler   N. one who sells goods in large quantities (The *wholesaler* stored merchandise in a large warehouse.)

Exercise 1
Write the letter of the word that best completes the sentence.

1. As a(n) _____, she sells truckloads of carpet.   _____
   A. usher   B. wholesaler   C. biochemist   D. dispatcher

2. Because she didn't enjoy being a lawyer, she decided to choose another _____.   _____
   A. warden   B. darkroom   C. vocation   D. mason

3. Every _____ for the job was a high school graduate.
   A. engraver   B. brigadier   C. executive   D. applicant   _____

4. The trophy was given to a(n) _____ to carve the winner's name on the base.
   A. engraver   B. bacteriologist   C. warden   D. broker   _____

5. As a stock _____, his job is to buy and sell stocks.
   A. applicant   B. chaplain   C. broker   D. aviator   _____

6. The sergeant was eventually promoted to the rank of a _____.
   A. corporal   B. brigadier   C. chaplain   D. vocation   _____

7. You might become a(n) _____ if you are interested in the causes of diseases.
   A. aviator   B. engraver   C. warden   D. bacteriologist   _____

8. All companies look for _____ in their employees.
   A. efficiency   B. executive   C. vocation   D. applicant   _____

9. The private became a _____, but she was still not a commissioned officer.
   A. administrator   B. corporal   C. brigadier   D. dispatcher   _____

10. Only the photographer stayed in the _____ while the film was developing.
    A. darkroom   B. vocation   C. mason   D. usher   _____

11. At the opera, a(n) _____ showed us to our seats.
    A. mason   B. biochemist   C. usher   D. chaplain   _____

12. The train _____ was careful to send each train out on time.
    A. aviator   B. dispatcher   C. executive   D. broker   _____

13. The _____ studied the structures of fats and proteins found in the human body.
    A. aviator   B. biochemist   C. executive   D. brigadier   _____

14. The principal is a(n) _____ in our school.
    A. aviator   B. broker   C. administrator   D. corporal   _____

15. There is more than one _____ in most large companies.
    A. executive   B. engraver   C. biochemist   D. warden   _____

Exercise 2

Write the letter of the word pair that has a relationship similar to the relationship of the first word pair.

16. **aviator : airplane : :**   A. fly : pilot   C. driver : car   _____
         B. air : bird   D. bus : passenger

17. **warden : prison : :**   A. waiter : customer   C. window : house   _____
         B. captain : ship   D. dog : kennel

18. **apprenticeship : skill : :**   A. study : subject   C. hand : mouth   _____
         B. bargain : sale   D. wide : long

19. **mason : stone : :**   A. high : low   C. painter : paint   _____
         B. lonely : sad   D. film : camera

20. **chaplain : religion : :**   A. janitor : clean   C. glove : hand   _____
         B. doctor : medicine   D. curved : round

Lesson 27
Actions

All the words in this lesson may be associated with actions.

alight   V. to settle onto or to get down from (Do you think the bird will *alight* on that branch?)

balk   V. to refuse to move (The dog will *balk* if you pull too hard on the leash.)

contort   V. to twist out of normal shape (The gymnast can *contort* her body by bending so far backwards that she can look through her legs.)

crumple   V. to crush into wrinkles (If you *crumple* the newspaper into a ball, you can toss it into the wastebasket.)

dangle   V. to hang in a loose enough manner to allow a swinging motion (Tie up the light cord so it won't *dangle* in your face.)

decline   V. to refuse (I don't want to go to the party, so I think I will *decline* the invitation.)

embrace   V. to hug (Jenny opened her arms to *embrace* her grandmother.)

entangle   V. to snarl or trap (As an insect struggles to get free of the spider's web, it will only *entangle* itself further in the sticky threads.)

fidget   V. to move about impatiently (As the speaker droned on, the child began to swing his feet and *fidget* in his seat.)

flounder   V. to struggle in an awkward way (Stumbling and flailing his arms, he began to *flounder* as he tried to run through the tall grass.)

frolic   V. to play in a carefree manner (You can hear the children laugh as they *frolic* happily in the shallow water.)

hack   V. to cut crudely and unevenly (You were supposed to slice the meat, not *hack* it to pieces.)

inspire   V. to fill with feeling or desire (A warm day will almost always *inspire* us to go on a picnic.)

intrude   V. to enter without being invited (I didn't want to *intrude* on his privacy so I didn't go in.)

mingle   V. to mix; to come together (She wanted to *mingle* with the guests at the party because she loved talking to many different people.)

mutilate   V. to damage or disfigure (In the art gallery, vandals tried to *mutilate* the famous painting by slicing it with a knife.)

pacify   V. to calm down; to make peaceful (The sheriff tried to *pacify* the angry crowd by assuring them that the killer would be brought to justice.)

pantomime   V. to act out in movements with no words (He lifted an imaginary fork as he tried to *pantomime* a person eating dinner.)

propel   V. to cause to move forward (The powerful rocket will *propel* the aircraft into orbit.)

pursue   V. to proceed with; to be involved in (He always said he wanted to *pursue* a career in teaching.)

Exercise 1
Write the letter of the word that best completes the sentence.

1. She used the dull ax to _____ away at the dead tree.
   A. mingle   B. hack   C. balk   D. embrace   _____

2. If your horse begins to _____, just kick it in the ribs to make it go.
   A. alight   B. propel   C. contort   D. balk   _____

3. There is no speaking in the play because the actors _____ their parts.
   A. pantomime   B. hack   C. dangle   D. alight   _____

4. In biology class, Sara refused to _____ the starfish by cutting off its leg.
   A. embrace   B. flounder   C. balk   D. mutilate

5. He saw the child _____ from the tree branch, holding on with one hand.
   A. mingle   B. dangle   C. intrude   D. propel

6. As she began to _____ from the train, she tripped and fell down the steps.
   A. alight   B. pursue   C. entangle   D. decline

7. The father ran to _____ his long lost daughter.
   A. intrude   B. propel   C. mingle   D. embrace

8. He could twist and _____ his face into strange shapes.
   A. hack   B. contort   C. frolic   D. entangle

9. I hate to _____ on him because he does not like to be disturbed when he is reading.
   A. intrude   B. pacify   C. inspire   D. balk

10. When the boat tipped over, she began to _____ in the deep water because she did not know how to swim.
    A. embrace   B. alight   C. crumple   D. flounder

Exercise 2

Write the letter of the word that most nearly has the *opposite* meaning of the italicized word.

11. **decline**   A. lower   B. accept   C. reject   D. avoid

12. **fidget**   A. relax   B. pause   C. hesitate   D. delay

13. **crumple**   A. roll   B. cut   C. throw   D. smooth

14. **entangle**   A. slip   B. unsnarl   C. allow   D. twist

15. **frolic**   A. jump   B. carry   C. spin   D. work

16. **inspire**   A. discourage   B. present   C. find   D. simplify

17. **mingle**   A. combine   B. join   C. blend   D. separate

18. **pacify**   A. sing   B. anger   C. lull   D. tie

19. **propel**   A. drive   B. bounce   C. restrain   D. urge

20. **pursue**   A. avoid   B. hit   C. control   D. slice

Lesson 28
Health

All the words in this lesson may be associated with health.

appease   V. to relieve (You should *appease* your thirst with water rather than with carbonated drinks.)

comparable   ADJ. having like traits (There is little difference in the cost because the two insurance plans have *comparable* rates.)

devote   V. to give one's time, effort, or attention to a person or purpose (Daphne will *devote* twenty minutes every morning to her exercise program.)

effect   N. something brought about by a cause (The *effect* of Wen's healthy diet should be an increase in energy.)

endurance   N. the power to last or keep on going (Flora wins short distance races, but does not have the *endurance* to run marathons.)

energetic   ADJ. full of energy (Many people claim that exercise makes them feel more *energetic*, rather than fatigued.)

hygiene   N. the science that deals with good health (The doctor's knowledge of *hygiene* helped him stop the epidemic.)

immunity   N. resistance to disease (Because his *immunity* to disease is low, he catches colds easily.)

inadequate   ADJ. not as much as required (Because of the *inadequate* supply of measles vaccine, some children will not be vaccinated.)

ingest   V. to take into the body for digestion (Because she is a vegetarian, Hiroko will *ingest* no red meat.)

limber   ADJ. bending easily (Her body was so *limber* that she could do backbends and splits with ease.)

maximum   N. the greatest possible amount (Janna's new diet limits her to a *maximum* of three small meals per day.)

nourishment   N. food and other substances needed to sustain life (For *nourishment* they brought carrots and peanuts along on the hike.)

omit   V. to leave out (If you *omit* the salad from tonight's menu, we won't have a green and leafy vegetable.)

requirement   N. something that is needed (The daily *requirement* for vitamin C can be fulfilled by eating a variety of citrus fruits.)

respiration   N. the act of inhaling and exhaling (On the mountain hike, *respiration* became more difficult as the air became thinner.)

rigorous   ADJ. very severe; harsh (The athletes were exhausted by the *rigorous* schedule of three practices a day.)

sane   ADJ. mentally healthy (The busy executive says she would go crazy without quiet weekends in the country to keep her *sane*.)

supplement   V. to supply what is lacking (Because she needs more iron, she will *supplement* her diet with iron tablets.)

vigor   N. healthy strength (He worked with such energy and *vigor*, it was clear he was fully recovered from the flu.)

Exercise 1
Write the letter of the word that best completes the sentence.

1. Coming to practice every day was a strict _____ of the track team.
   A. hygiene   B. effect   C. requirement   D. maximum

2. The athletes were told to _____ their diets with extra vitamins and minerals.
   A. supplement   B. appease   C. omit   D. ingest

3. The swimmer had great _____ and did not tire easily. _____

   A. effect   B. endurance   C. respiration   D. immunity

4. The relation between emotional and physical health is described in the saying, "a _____
   _____ mind and a healthy body."

   A. sane   B. limber   C. comparable   D. rigorous

5. A basic course in _____ will teach you how to maintain your good health. _____

   A. endurance   B. immunity   C. maximum   D. hygiene

6. Lack of sleep can lower your _____ to contagious diseases. _____

   A. maximum   B. requirement   C. immunity   D. nourishment

7. She has become quite _____ after ten minutes of stretching every morning. _____

   A. comparable   B. sane   C. rigorous   D. limber

8. While the ankle is healing, she can only run a _____ of two miles a day. _____

   A. effect   B. hygiene   C. maximum   D. respiration

9. There is more real _____ in an apple than in a sack of potato chips. _____

   A. hygiene   B. nourishment   C. endurance   D. respiration

10. According to the _____ training schedule, the gymnasts will be practicing six _____
    hours a day.

   A. rigorous   B. limber   C. sane   D. comparable

Exercise 2

Write the letter of the word that most nearly has the *same* meaning as the italicized
word.

11. *omit*	A. permit	B. exclude	C. accuse	D. seem	_____
12. *devote*	A. dedicate	B. believe	C. take	D. lead	_____
13. *vigor*	A. sleepiness	B. truth	C. energy	D. permission	_____
14. *comparable*	A. similar	B. believable	C. peaceful	D. predictable	_____
15. *energetic*	A. bored	B. large	C. polluted	D. lively	_____
16. *ingest*	A. exceed	B. choke	C. eat	D. hurry	_____
17. *appease*	A. join	B. allow	C. satisfy	D. accumulate	_____
18. *inadequate*	A. slow	B. insufficient	C. soft	D. healthy	_____
19. *respiration*	A. ache	B. appetite	C. perspiration	D. breathing	_____
20. *effect*	A. result	B. permission	C. opening	D. cause	_____

Lesson 29
Art and Music

All the words in this lesson may be associated with art and music.

aesthetic   ADJ. having to do with beauty or the appreciation of beauty (Art and music are *aesthetic* interests, while politics and economics are not.)

anthem   N. a song of praise or patriotism (The crowd sang the country's national *anthem* before the game.)

attentive   ADJ. showing attention (The *attentive* audience watched the musician closely.)

clarity   N. clearness (The *clarity* of his playing allowed you to hear every note.)

diorama   N. an exhibit with life-like figures in front and a painting in the background (At the museum we saw clay models of cave men sitting around a fire in the *diorama* of prehistoric life.)

inspiration   N. an impulse or idea (His *inspiration* for the play was a children's story that he had read long ago.)

lyrics   N. the words of a song (I can remember the melody of the song, but I've forgotten the *lyrics.*)

maestro   N. a master in a field of art, especially music (Because of his many years as a great pianist, students came to the *maestro* for advice about their careers.)

merit   N. excellence, value (We think your ideas about the concert have *merit,* so we will discuss them in our meeting.)

perspective   N. the art of representing objects on a flat surface to make them look like they have depth and distance (The artist created *perspective* in the picture by making the railroad tracks come closer together at the horizon.)

portrait   N. a painting or picture of a person (A *portrait* of my grandfather is hanging in the hall.)

profile   N. a side view of a human face (A *profile* of his face showed his hooked nose.)

promotional   ADJ. having to do with furthering the development of something (The main purpose of the singer's *promotional* tour was to advertise his new record.)

psalm   N. a hymn or poem of praise (The choir sang a *psalm* during the church service.)

rarity   N. something rare or uncommon (There are many talented musicians, but true musical genius is a *rarity.*)

replay   V. to play again (We will *replay* the tape several times to listen for mistakes.)

soprano   ADJ. having a high voice (Her *soprano* voice rang clear and true above the lower alto parts.)

sustain   V. to keep on; to keep in effect (By taking a deep breath, he was able to *sustain* the note for almost half a minute.)

tempera   N. a type of painting in which the colors are mixed with egg white or yolk instead of oil (Sometimes he paints with *tempera,* but he prefers using oils.)

tinge   V. to color with a slight amount (If you *tinge* the yellow with blue, it will begin to look green.)

Exercise 1
Write the letter of the word that best completes the sentence.

1. The _____ of ancient Egypt contained figures of Egyptian workers in front of a painting of a pyramid.   _____
   A. rarity   B. tempera   C. diorama   D. psalm

2. Her voice was definitely high enough to sing in the _____ section of the choir.   _____
   A. soprano   B. promotional   C. aesthetic   D. attentive

3. We sing the school _____ after every basketball game.
   A. diorama   B. anthem   C. rarity   D. profile   _____

4. Francis Scott Key got the _____ for "The Star Spangled Banner" during the War of 1812.   _____
   A. inspiration   B. tempera   C. psalm   D. profile

5. The official _____ of each governor hangs in the state house.   _____
   A. profile   B. portrait   C. lyrics   D. merit

6. We all must learn the _____ if we are going to sing the song in the show.   _____
   A. merit   B. perspective   C. lyrics   D. anthem

7. The artist mixed several shades of _____ for the painting.   _____
   A. maestro   B. diorama   C. perspective   D. tempera

8. On the whole, the song has _____, but the melody still needs work.   _____
   A. merit   B. portrait   C. inspiration   D. psalm

9. He bought the painting for _____ reasons, not because of the money he would make.   _____
   A. attentive   B. aesthetic   C. soprano   D. promotional

10. Through the artist's use of _____, the mountains in the painting seemed far away.   _____
    A. profile   B. maestro   C. lyrics   D. perspective

11. A voice like hers is a _____ in the field of rock music.   _____
    A. tempera   B. rarity   C. merit   D. perspective

12. When the _____ became too old to give concerts, he taught young violinists.   _____
    A. maestro   B. portrait   C. anthem   D. psalm

13. The _____ posters advertised the concert.   _____
    A. attentive   B. aesthetic   C. soprano   D. promotional

14. She wanted only her _____ painted, not a full view of her face.   _____
    A. merit   B. lyrics   C. profile   D. diorama

15. He read verses of the _____ in the Bible.   _____
    A. tempera   B. psalm   C. rarity   D. profile

Exercise 2

Write the letter of the word pair that has a relationship similar to the relationship of the first word pair.

16. **attentive : unobserving : :**   A. silly : foolish   C. fish : stew   _____
                                             B. hot : cold   D. light : sun

17. **clarity : clear : :**   A. sweet : sour   C. path : trail   _____
                                     B. corn : corner   D. beauty : beautiful

18. **sustain : hold : :**   A. happy : joyful   C. glove : hand   _____
                                    B. car : driver   D. cow : milk

19. **replay : sonata : :**   A. reread : novel   C. real : unreal   _____
                                     B. return : trip   D. hop : sit

20. **tinge : color : :**   A. dog : collar   C. season : salt   _____
                                   B. wheel : round   D. fall : trip

Lesson 30
Science

All the words in this lesson may be associated with science.

absorption N. the act of taking in or soaking up (Although a rag will soak up water, *absorption* will be greater if you use a sponge.)

aeronautical ADJ. having to do with the design, manufacture, and operation of aircraft (When he was an *aeronautical* engineer, he designed airplanes.)

aerospace N. a field of science having to do with the flight of spacecraft beyond the earth's atmosphere (Her studies of *aerospace* convinced her to become an astronaut.)

analyze V. to find out about something by separating it into parts (If you *analyze* water, you will find that it is made of hydrogen and oxygen.)

biological ADJ. having to do with plant and animal life (*Biological* sciences are concerned with living things.)

biophysics N. the study of the relation of plants and animals to physical processes (When studying *biophysics,* she learned how the body retains heat.)

decompose V. to rot (The leaves will *decompose* over time and can be used as fertilizer.)

distillation N. the process of purifying a liquid by heating until it becomes a gas and then cooling it until it is again in liquid form (Through *distillation,* it is possible to separate the salt from sea water.)

dormant ADJ. not active for some period of time (The volcano was *dormant* for the fifty years between its eruptions.)

geological ADJ. having to do with the study of the history of the earth (The *geological* team examined the layers of rock to determine when the mountain was formed.)

inquiry N. the act of asking (Our *inquiry* about the science lab was answered promptly.)

infinite ADJ. without limits (We assume that space is *infinite* because no one has proven that it has a boundary.)

magnify V. to make a thing look bigger than it actually is (Use the microscope to *magnify* the mosquito larva so you can see it more clearly.)

observatory N. place from which the stars and planets are studied (Through the huge telescope at the *observatory,* the stars seem very close.)

ozone N. a form of oxygen produced by extreme heat or electricity (The *ozone* in the upper layer of the earth's atmosphere filters out harmful rays.)

realm N. a specific field (The *realm* of science includes chemistry and astronomy.)

scientific ADJ. having to do with science (A *scientific* experiment requires close observation and careful recording of information.)

simulation N. the act of putting on the appearance of something else (During the flight *simulation,* pictures and sounds made the astronaut feel as if he were piloting a real rocket.)

specimen N. one of a group used to represent the group (Each *specimen* represents a different family of insect.)

vaporize V. to cause to change to a gaseous state (Water will *vaporize* and turn to steam when it is heated.)

Exercise 1
Write the letter of the word that best completes the sentence.

1. At the _____ we heard a lecture about the moon.
   A. simulation   B. observatory   C. biophysics   D. aerospace

2. When we studied _____, we learned about the strength and durability of bones. _____
   A. ozone   B. inquiry   C. absorption   D. biophysics

3. An _____ engineer must know many things about airplanes and flight. _____
   A. geological   B. aeronautical   C. biological   D. magnified

4. The law of gravity is a _____ theory. _____
   A. scientific   B. infinite   C. biological   D. dormant

5. Study of the _____ of light by different materials has helped us understand how _____
   colors are produced.
   A. aerospace   B. absorption   C. observatory   D. realm

6. The _____ researcher predicted the earthquake. _____
   A. geological   B. infinite   C. biological   D. aeronautical

7. The layer of _____ that surrounds our planet is very important to our survival. _____
   A. realm   B. aerospace   C. ozone   D. simulation

8. The _____ sciences can teach us about the animals that share the planet with us. _____
   A. aeronautical   B. biological   C. geological   D. magnified

9. If the gasoline spills, it may _____ and become highly explosive. _____
   A. decompose   B. analyze   C. vaporize   D. magnify

10. A career in _____ requires an understanding of how a spacecraft acts in the _____
    space beyond our atmosphere.
    A. aerospace   B. absorption   C. inquiry   D. realm

Exercise 2

Write the letter of the word that most nearly has the *same* meaning as the italicized
word.

11. *simulation*   A. imitation   B. actuality   C. fact   D. existing   _____
12. *analyze*   A. ignore   B. disregard   C. overlook   D. examine   _____
13. *inquiry*   A. response   B. question   C. retort   D. reply   _____
14. *specimen*   A. rock   B. type   C. class   D. sample   _____
15. *dormant*   A. smooth   B. hurried   C. inactive   D. fantastic   _____
16. *infinite*   A. endless   B. proven   C. alone   D. less   _____
17. *realm*   A. area   B. food   C. king   D. idea   _____
18. *magnify*   A. feed   B. pour   C. cut   D. enlarge   _____
19. *distillation*   A. disease   B. purification C. force   D. color   _____
20. *decompose*   A. race   B. sleep   C. decay   D. freshen   _____

Lesson 31
Hobbies

All the words in this lesson may be associated with hobbies.

approval   N. favorable opinion; consent (Before he can go skiing, he must get the *approval* of his parents.)

billow   V. to swell out (As the wind fills the limp sails, they will *billow* into curves.)

burnish   V. to make shiny by rubbing (Julia used a fine wire brush to *burnish* the metal until it glowed.)

certification   N. a spoken, written, or printed statement declaring something to be true (After passing the test, Lee received his *certification* as a life guard.)

deflate   V. to let air or gas out (You can *deflate* your bike tires by allowing air to escape from the valve.)

doldrums   N. a period of inactivity or low spirits (If you're discouraged or in the *doldrums,* you should find a new hobby to cheer you up.)

exhilarate   V. to make cheerful, lively, or excited (Taking a bicycle ride in the brisk morning air will *exhilarate* us.)

filigree   N. a delicate, lacelike ornamental work of twisted gold or silver wire (He makes earrings of *filigree* by twisting fine gold wires into intricate shapes.)

guppy   N. a small, brightly colored fish of tropical fresh water, commonly raised in aquariums (Rich bought a *guppy* to add to the tropical fish in his aquarium.)

malfunction   N. to fail to function (The *malfunction* of the drill was caused by a bad electrical connection.)

manipulate   V. to handle or treat skillfully (Henry took lessons to learn how to *manipulate* the glider in a strong wind.)

marina   N. a dock or harbor where supplies and repair facilities are available for boats (We dropped anchor at the *marina* so we could fix the broken rudder.)

marionette   N. a small doll or figure fitted with strings that are moved from above (By pulling on its strings, Ana made the *marionette* walk across the stage of the puppet theater.)

memoir   N. an account of experiences through which the author has lived (Miss Marchesi's *memoir* tells about growing up in Africa.)

participation   N. taking part (Shawna's *participation* in sports means she must attend practice every day after school.)

pastime   N. something that serves to make time pass by pleasantly (Our family's favorite *pastime* is reading.)

pedigree   N. a list of the ancestors of a purebred animal (Because Lana's dog is well trained and has a fine *pedigree,* it wins awards in dog shows.)

submerge   V. to put under water (After practicing holding her breath, the skin diver can *submerge* for as long as a minute.)

sculpture   N. the art of carving or modeling figures (Maureen made a clay *sculpture* of a dolphin.)

vegetation   N. plant life (The *vegetation* in his garden included wildflowers and weeds.)

Exercise 1
Write the letter of the word that best completes the sentence.

1. A _____ cannot live in water that is too cold.

   A. guppy   B. marionette   C. marina   D. pedigree   _____

2. Since _____ in the school hobby show was required, Joel entered his model plane.

   A. doldrums   B. vegetation   C. approval   D. participation

3. They docked the boat in the _____ after sailing in the bay.
   A. memoir   B. marina   C. pedigree   D. malfunction   _____

4. We made designs in silver _____ in art class.
   A. memoir   B. certification   C. filigree   D. pastime   _____

5. A _____ in the engine caused the motorboat to lose speed.
   A. marina   B. malfunction   C. filigree   D.sculpture   _____

6. A gloomy day with nothing to do can put you in the _____.
   A. filigree   B. marionette   C. pedigree   D. doldrums   _____

7. You need proper _____ to become a flying instructor.
   A. marina   B. pedigree   C. billow   D. certification   _____

8. After she carved the wooden _____, she rubbed it with oil.
   A. vegetation   B. certification   C. sculpture   D. filigree   _____

9. The _____ for John's horse includes a famous race horse.
   A. marina   B. marionette   C. pastime   D. pedigree   _____

10. To find the leak in the inner tube, _____ it in a pan of water and look for bubbles.
    A. submerge   B. billow   C. burnish   D. exhilarate   _____

Exercise 2

Write the letter of the word that most nearly has the *same* meaning as the italicized word.

11. *deflate*   A. collapse   B. enjoy   C. enlarge   D. invent   _____

12. *manipulate*   A. increase   B. empty   C. operate   D. declare   _____

13. *marionette*   A. fish   B. exhaustion   C. happiness   D. puppet   _____

14. *pastime*   A. hobby   B. job   C. employer   D. mistake   _____

15. *exhilarate*   A. lose   B. anger   C. enliven   D. forget   _____

16. *vegetation*   A. soil   B. plants   C. tools   D. breakfast   _____

17. *burnish*   A. reduce   B. announce   C. polish   D. mix   _____

18. *billow*   A. bulge   B. direct   C. finish   D. disappear   _____

19. *approval*   A. lift   B. drink   C. okay   D. mend   _____

20. *memoir*   A. alphabet   B. dictionary   C. fairy tale   D. biography   _____

Lesson 32
Business

All the words in this lesson may be associated with business.

administer   V. to be in charge of or manage (Avery's father will *administer* the research department of the company.)

advancement   N. moving up to a higher level (Because there are opportunities for *advancement* in the company, he will have chances to move to better positions.)

bureaucracy   N. a management system with many departments and subdivisions (The large *bureaucracy* in the firm meant that it often took days for a request to get from one office to another.)

certainty   N. freedom from doubt (Shoppers look for a reasonable price and the *certainty* that the product is good.)

chairperson   N. the one who is in charge of a meeting or committee (The *chairperson* called the meeting to order.)

clout   N. strong influence (Richard will use his *clout* with the boss to make sure his friend gets the job.)

commercial   ADJ. having profit as a primary goal (The play won awards but it was not a *commercial* success because few people bought tickets.)

compensate   V. to pay for work or goods (If you do a good job, I will *compensate* you for your work.)

complimentary   ADJ. free (The food company gave away *complimentary* boxes of their new cereal.)

formidable   ADJ. awesome in size, difficulty, strength, etc. (Because the company was in so much debt, there were *formidable* odds against making a profit.)

guarantee   V. to promise that a product will be repaired or replaced if it turns out not to work properly (The manufacturer will pay for the broken radio because they *guarantee* it for two years.)

import   V. to bring into a country goods or materials from another country (The United States continues to *import* cars made in Japan and Germany.)

negotiate   V. to deal or bargain with others (The supermarket employees met with the manager to *negotiate* a raise.)

organize   V. to coordinate separate parts into a well-functioning whole (Mrs. Fisher's class will *organize* the spring bake sale by assigning duties to each homeroom.)

pamphlet   N. a short booklet (The salesman gave us a six-page *pamphlet* describing the features of the computer.)

pompous   ADJ. overly serious and self-important (The president gave a *pompous* speech congratulating himself on the company's progress.)

trustee   N. one of a group of people appointed to manage a company or organization (As a *trustee* of the hospital, Ms. Stone advises administrators on their budgets.)

upstart   N. a person who rises suspiciously quickly to power or wealth (Because he is so young to be a supervisor, Ricardo is considered an *upstart* by some employees.)

voluminous   ADJ. of very large size or amount (The inventor was surprised by the *voluminous* pile of mail praising his new mousetrap.)

wholesale   ADJ. the lower price charged for large quantities of goods sold to stores for resale to individual customers (If the grocer charges the *wholesale* price for food, he won't make money.)

Exercise 1
Write the letter of the word set that best completes the sentence.

1. The advertising states that the _____ will personally _____ the car.   _____
   A. chairperson — guarantee   C. bureaucracy — import
   B. advancement — organize   D. clout — compensate

2. There are _____ problems with management, but the workers will _____ to avoid a strike.
   A. pompous — import
   B. commercial — administer
   C. formidable — negotiate
   D. complimentary — guarantee

3. The new president will _____ the company better by reducing its _____.
   A. compensate — pamphlet
   B. administer — bureaucracy
   C. negotiate — clout
   D. guarantee — trustee

4. Kyle is proud of his rapid _____, but is regarded as a(n) _____ by coworkers.
   A. advancement — upstart
   B. clout — advancement
   C. bureaucracy — certainty
   D. certainty — pamphlet

5. To qualify for the _____ price you must purchase a _____ quantity.
   A. formidable — commercial
   B. wholesale — voluminous
   C. complimentary — pompous
   D. pompous — wholesale

6. The blender came with a(n) _____ describing how to receive a _____ cookbook.
   A. chairperson — pompous
   B. pamphlet — complimentary
   C. upstart — formidable
   D. advancement — voluminous

7. Mr. Adams will _____ the expert for his advice about how to _____ the factory.
   A. import — negotiate
   B. organize — import
   C. administer — guarantee
   D. compensate — organize

8. The _____ is well-liked, but I think he is _____ and self-satisfied.
   A. pamphlet — commercial
   B. trustee — voluminous
   C. trustee — pompous
   D. certainty — formidable

9. Amanda has a high degree of _____ that her invention will be a _____ success.
   A. chairman — complimentary
   B. certainty — commercial
   C. pamphlet — pompous
   D. bureaucracy — wholesale

10. The president used his _____ to get permission to _____ more sugar from Cuba.
    A. upstart — import
    B. clout — organize
    C. advancement — administer
    D. clout — import

Exercise 2

Write the letter of the word that most nearly has the *same* meaning as the italicized word.

11. *negotiate*	A. bargain	B. stop	C. mix	D. raise
12. *certainty*	A. height	B. doubt	C. confidence	D. dwelling
13. *administer*	A. direct	B. yell	C. preach	D. quote
14. *organize*	A. count	B. pay	C. loan	D. arrange
15. *pompous*	A. delicate	B. boastful	C. shy	D. dizzy
16. *advancement*	A. promotion	B. violence	C. risk	D. attitude
17. *clout*	A. nonsense	B. weapon	C. power	D. mother
18. *guarantee*	A. destroy	B. pledge	C. remove	D. tease
19. *pamphlet*	A. napkin	B. ribbon	C. joke	D. leaflet
20. *chairperson*	A. chief	B. rider	C. police	D. actor

Lesson 33
Animal Life

All the words in this lesson may be associated with animal life.

constrict V. to make smaller by squeezing (The tight collar may *constrict* the dog's throat and make breathing difficult.)

hibernate V. to sleep or be inactive during the winter (When a bear begins to *hibernate,* its heart rate slows and it scarcely moves.)

inhumane ADJ. lacking in kindness or mercy (Some people feel it is *inhumane* to kill an animal for sport.)

loll V. to lie or lean in a lazy manner (On a hot summer day, the cat will *loll* in the shade, showing little interest in chasing birds.)

lope V. to run with a long, easy stride (They watched the long-legged giraffe *lope* across the grassy plain.)

mallard N. a type of wild duck with a green neck and head (The *mallard* made its nest in the reeds by the pond.)

parasite N. an animal or plant that lives on another (The leech is a *parasite* that survives by sucking the blood of other animals.)

pelt N. the skin of a fur-bearing animal (The trapper skinned the deer and used the *pelt* to make a jacket.)

potential ADJ. possible, capable of being (Because it has a such a sweet disposition, the stray dog has the *potential* for being a good pet.)

primate N. the most highly developed mammals (A monkey is one example of a *primate.*)

scanty ADJ. not enough; meager (Grass for grazing was *scanty* so there are few deer in the area.)

slacken V. to become slower (Even the fastest deer will eventually tire and *slacken* its pace.)

slay V. to kill (The hunter promised himself that he would *slay* the wild boar and bring its head back as a trophy.)

survive V. to continue to live (The camel can *survive* for many days in the desert without water.)

thwart V. to block; to prevent from taking place (A porcupine will curl into a prickly ball to *thwart* an enemy looking for prey.)

tolerable ADJ. bearable; endurable (Amy found that riding the camel was a *tolerable,* but not particularly comfortable, means of travel.)

tormentor N. one who causes great pain (The boy who teased the dog was a *tormentor* of other small animals as well.)

tusk N. a very long, projecting tooth (The elephant can use its *tusk* to lift objects.)

vermin N. one of a class of small animals and insects that are destructive or injurious to health (Inside the filthy shack were rats, cockroaches, and other *vermin.*)

wily ADJ. sly; crafty (The *wily* fox slunk quietly through the grass towards the unsuspecting rabbit.)

Exercise 1
Write the letter of the word that best completes the sentence.

1. The heat was not _____, so the dog jumped into the cool pond for some relief.   _____

    A. scanty   B. wily   C. tolerable   D. inhumane

2. Many people protest the _____ treatment of animals used in scientific experiments.   _____

    A. inhumane   B. scanty   C. wily   D. tolerable

3. The Plains Indians would _____ buffalo for food and clothing. _____
   A. constrict   B. thwart   C. hibernate   D. slay

4. Even though the shelter was _____, it saved the horse from freezing in the _____
   blizzard.
   A. tolerable   B. scanty   C. wily   D. inhumane

5. The cat in the barn helps keep the _____ population under control. _____
   A. tusk   B. vermin   C. primate   D. pelt

6. My mother's favorite _____ at the zoo is the baby chimpanzee. _____
   A. primate   B. tusk   C. vermin   D. parasite

7. Many shore birds did not _____ the great oil spill. _____
   A. lope   B. slacken   C. loll   D. survive

8. The flea is a bothersome _____ for many cats and dogs. _____
   A. pelt   B. potential   C. parasite   D. tusk

9. The young _____ chased the small kitten around and around the house. _____
   A. tormentor   B. mallard   C. parasite   D. vermin

10. After realizing he was no longer being followed, the frightened raccoon began to _____
    _____ its pace.
    A. thwart   B. survive   C. slacken   D. lope

11. Some scientists think that seaweed has the _____ for becoming a major source of _____
    animal food.
    A. vermin   B. primate   C. mallard   D. potential

12. The mouse scurried under a log to _____ the cat's attack. _____
    A. slacken   B. thwart   C. constrict   D. slay

13. We watched a lone_____ swim across the lake and then fly away. _____
    A. mallard   B. primate   C. parasite   D. tormentor

14. We could see the dog _____ on the sunny porch with its eyes closed. _____
    A. thwart   B. lope   C. slacken   D. loll

15. Bears, skunks, and ground squirrels are animals that _____ in the winter. _____
    A. hibernate   B. constrict   C. lope   D. slay

Exercise 2

Write the letter of the word pair that has a relationship similar to the relationship of the
first word pair.

16. *wily : sly : :*   A. city : town   C. off : on   _____
                              B. glove : hand   D. story : read

17. *pelt : fox : :*   A. brother : boy   C. feathers : duck   _____
                              B. win : lose   D. bear : den

18. *constrict : expand : :*   A. gun : gallop   C. car : driver   _____
                                      B. engine : go   D. friend : enemy

19. *lope : cheetah : :*   A. hop : rabbit   C. kind : cruel   _____
                                  B. bird : sky   D. three : six

20. *tusk : elephant : :*   A. glass : break   C. small : tiny   _____
                                   B. molar : person   D. left : right

Lesson 34
Prefixes — di-/dis-

All the words in this lesson contain the Latin prefixes *di-* or *dis-*, which mean "the opposite or absence of."

disable   V. to weaken or cripple (They tried to *disable* the engine by taking out the spark plug.)

disabuse   V. to correct a false impression (I will *disabuse* you of the notion that my dress was expensive by telling you how much it cost.)

disburse   V. to pay out (The cashier will *disburse* refund money to people who have returned defective merchandise.)

discord   N. lack of harmony or agreement (There was *discord* among the committee members because each favored a different plan.)

discredit   V. to throw doubt on (Maria will *discredit* Tom's story about being at the library when she reports seeing him at the video store.)

disgorge   V. to discharge contents with force; to pour forth (During an eruption, a volcano will *disgorge* hot lava and mud from its center.)

disgrace   N. loss of respect or honor (Yoriko is in *disgrace* for wrecking the car.)

disheartened   ADJ. without hope or the spirit to go on (The *disheartened* boy gave up trying when he realized that he would never finish the assignment on time.)

disintegration   N. the process of falling apart (The *disintegration* of the picnic table was caused by being left out in bad weather for many years.)

dismantle   V. to take apart (The boys will have to *dismantle* Matt's bike to make it fit into the car.)

disparity   N. a difference (There is a great *disparity* in the heights of Ed and Juan, because Juan is so much taller than Ed.)

dispassionate   ADJ. without emotion; calm (Even though she felt strongly about the issues, her speech was *dispassionate* and reasonable.)

disposable   ADJ. made to be thrown away after one or a few uses (Glenn wants *disposable* plates for the party so he won't have to wash dishes.)

disrobe   V. to take off one's clothes (After falling into the pond, it was necessary for Alex to *disrobe* and put on dry clothes.)

dissent   N. difference of opinion; disagreement (The angry muttering of the crowd signaled that there was *dissent* among the people.)

dissipate   V. to spend or use wastefully (By gambling on horses and cards, the young man was able to *dissipate* the family fortune in several years.)

dissuade   V. to advise against (I will try to *dissuade* you from swimming too far out in the bay.)

distraction   N. something that prevents concentration (Her brother's trumpet playing is a *distraction* when Renee is doing her homework.)

divergent   ADJ. differing; branching off (Even though the class had *divergent* opinions about where to go on the field trip, they were able to agree on what food to take.)

diversion   N. a pleasant activity that gives relief from work or worry (In the middle of exam week, Tod went to the movies as a *diversion*.)

Exercise 1
Write the letter of the word that best completes the sentence.

1. Her gloomy and discouraged face showed that she was _____ about losing the race.   _____
   A. dispassionate   B. disheartened   C. divergent   D.disposable

2. His broken leg will _____ the skier for the rest of the winter.   _____
   A. dismantle   B. disburse   C. disabuse   D. disable

3. No decision was made because _____ opinions made it impossible to come to an agreement. _____
   A. divergent   B. disheartened   C. disposable   D. dispassionate

4. The lawyer tried to _____ the witness's testimony by proving he was a liar. _____
   A. dismantle   B. dissuade   C. discredit   D. disrobe

5. New bricks and mortar were added to help stop the _____ of the old wall. _____
   A. disparity   B. disintegration   C. diversion   D. dissent

6. Going to the beach is a _____ that will take your mind off your troubles. _____
   A. disparity   B. dissent   C. diversion   D. discord

7. Please don't try to _____ me from going, because I will not change my mind. _____
   A. dissuade   B. disrobe·   C. disabuse   D. dismantle

8. If we _____ our resources, there will be none for future generations. _____
   A. disable   B. dismantle   C. disabuse   D. dissipate

9. Because there was no _____, the motion was passed. _____
   A. distraction   B. diversion   C. disgrace   D. dissent

10. The _____ in the older and younger girls' ages makes it unlikely that they will be close friends. _____
    A. disgrace   B. disparity   C. discord   D. dissent

11. On the last day of camping trips, we _____ the tent and pack it in the trunk. _____
    A. disgorge   B. dismantle   C. disburse   D. disable

12. Her _____ announcement gave no clue that she was really very upset. _____
    A. divergent   B. disheartened   C. dispassionate   D. disposable

13. I will _____ you of the idea that you are the fastest runner by beating you in a race. _____
    A. disburse   B. disabuse   C. disable   D. dismantle

14. Hank feels that items that can be repaired are better than _____ ones. _____
    A. disposable   B. divergent   C. disheartened   D. dispassionate

15. There is no _____ in losing the tennis match if you did your best. _____
    A. disintegration   B. disgrace   C. dissent   D. diversion

Exercise 2
Write the letter of the word pair that has a relationship similar to the relationship of the first word pair.

16. **disgorge : vomit : :**   A. happy : sad   C. soft : blanket _____
                                    B. car : auto   D. foot : leg

17. **disburse : money : :**   A. sew : seeds   C. wheel : bike _____
                                    B. hat : head   D. open : shut

18. **disrobe : bath : :**   A. blouse : skirt   C. dress : party _____
                                    B. soap : clean   D. brush : paint

19. **distract : distraction : :** A. king : queen   C. street : path _____
                                    B. carry : carrier   D. final : finally

20. **discord : harmony : :**   A. spring : flower   C. pencil : paper _____
                                    B. sing : song   D. up : down

Lesson 35
Prefixes — co-/con-/com-

All the words in this lesson contain the prefixes *co-*, *con-*, or *com-*, which mean "together or with."

commemorate   V. to serve as a memorial or reminder (The statue of the pioneer will *commemorate* the town's first settlers.)

commentary   N. remarks that interpret or explain (In his *commentary*, the museum guide gave a brief analysis of each painting.)

commiserate   V. to express sympathy for someone (Jan's friend called to *commiserate* with her about being sick and missing the prom.)

communication   N. the expression of thoughts, feelings, or information (While he is at camp, Kyle stays in *communication* with his family by writing letters.)

commute   V. to travel back and forth regularly (Mr. Lopez lives in the country so he must *commute* to his job in the city.)

competence   N. having the skills or knowledge necessary to do a good job (Because she has no *competence* in the area of music, she will never become a concert pianist.)

complacent   ADJ. so pleased with yourself as to be unaware that things could change for the worse (If the team feels *complacent* because they are ahead, they may not play their best game.)

complexity   N. the state of having many parts (The *complexity* of the multi-step word problem is greater than that of the simple arithmetic equation.)

complicate   V. to make more difficult (It will *complicate* the shopping trip if we have to go to more than two stores.)

component   N. one part of a system that has many parts (The speakers are a new *component* for Kevin's stereo.)

compromise   V. to settle a dispute by each party's agreeing to accept some change (Elize and Mark will *compromise* by choosing another topic because neither likes the other's first choice.)

concise   ADJ. saying much with few words (Becky's *concise* summary of the chapter only took two paragraphs.)

condescend   V. to do something while acting as if it is beneath you (Even though I am worthy of more important activities, I will *condescend* to help you with your spelling words.)

confederate   N. a partner, especially in mischief (Zach was Kate's *confederate* in the prank.)

consist   V. to be made up (Our study group will *consist* of Jane, Kasmir, and myself.)

conspire   V. to plot together secretly (After school, Mark and Allen would *conspire* about where to have the secret club meeting.)

correlation   N. a relation in which one thing affects another thing (Our teacher feels there is a *correlation* between getting a good night's sleep and getting good grades.)

correspond   V. to be in agreement with (Each letter on the diagram will *correspond* to a part of the model airplane.)

corroborate   V. to provide evidence that agrees (Since John's account of the accident is the same as mine, it will *corroborate* my story.)

corrosion   N. a chemical process that eats away slowly, such as rust (The *corrosion* finally caused a leak in the rusty pipe.)

Exercise 1
Write the letter of the word that best completes the sentence.

1. Since we each speak a different language, _____ is sometimes difficult.   _____
   A. competence   B. communication   C. complexity   D. corrosion

2. There is a _____ between the weather and the number of visitors at the amusement park.   _____
   A. complexity   B. commentary   C. correlation   D. confederate

3. Meghan's mother likes to _____ to work because the train ride gives her time to read.   _____
   A. consist   B. conspire   C. complicate   D. commute

4. I must call Terri to _____ with her over the defeat of the soccer team.   _____
   A. commiserate   B. corroborate   C. commemorate   D. contort

5. By adding another character to his mystery story, Myles will _____ the plot.   _____
   A. compromise   B. commiserate   C. commute   D. complicate

6. The school newspaper contains lively _____ on school events.   _____
   A. complexity   B. corrosion   C. commentary   D. component

7. The key would not turn because of the _____ in the metal lock.   _____
   A. corrosion   B. complexity   C. communication   D. competence

8. Aaron assured the family that he had great _____ as a baby sitter.   _____
   A. confederate   B. competence   C. corrosion   D. commentary

9. Greg wants to _____ because he is tired of arguing.   _____
   A. complicate   B. consist   C. compromise   D. commute

10. The dinner will _____ of fish, rice, and salad.   _____
    A. consist   B. correspond   C. commiserate   D. conspire

Exercise 2

Write the letter of the word that most nearly has the *same* meaning as the italicized word.

11. *confederate*	A. actor	B. helper	C. driver	D. washer	_____
12. *complacent*	A. happy	B. sad	C. angry	D. satisfied	_____
13. *correspond*	A. hurry	B. match	C. help	D. disagree	_____
14. *condescend*	A. stoop	B. amuse	C. pull	D. meet	_____
15. *component*	A. pet	B. mirror	C. portion	D. teacher	_____
16. *conspire*	A. sing	B. hit	C. relax	D. plan	_____
17. *corroborate*	A. confirm	B. sell	C. deny	D. insist	_____
18. *commemorate*	A. destroy	B. plant	C. march	D. remember	_____
19. *complexity*	A. need	B. step	C. complication	D. view	_____
20. *concise*	A. silly	B. long	C. heavy	D. brief	_____

Lesson 36
Verbal Communication

All of the words in this lesson may be associated with verbal communication.

counsel N. advice or guidance from a knowledgeable person (Clara's older sister gave her good *counsel* about how to mix social life with school work.)

dictate V. to read something aloud so it can be written down (I will *dictate* the speech into the tape recorder so my secretary can type it.)

disparage V. to put down or belittle (When you constantly criticize her plans, you *disparage* her ideas.)

emanate V. to flow from a source (Many reports about the President *emanate* from the White House.)

enumerate V. to name one by one; count (I will list the proposals from the meeting as you *enumerate* them.)

exhort V. to urge or plead through strong argument (The leader of the rebellion will *exhort* the crowd to disobey the king.)

forceful ADJ. done with force (His *forceful* speech persuaded the committee to take action.)

garble V. to mix up; to confuse (The broken microphone will *garble* the words of the speaker.)

impede V. to obstruct or put obstacles in the way (By refusing to let him speak on the talk show, the station will *impede* free speech.)

inane ADJ. silly (The boy's *inane* remark seemed out of place in the serious discussion.)

inarticulate ADJ. unable to speak clearly or understandably (The *inarticulate* student could never find the right words to express his thoughts.)

keynote N. main idea (Our conference *keynote* was wildlife preservation.)

lecturer N. person who give speeches or talks on a chosen subject (The *lecturer* spoke to the audience about recycling.)

lisp N. a speech impediment; mispronunciation of the sounds of s and z (The small child spoke with a *lisp*, saying "thithter" instead of "sister.")

oration N. a formal speech (Lincoln gave his famous *oration* at Gettysburg in 1863.)

proclamation N. an official statement (In his *proclamation*, the king promised to free all political prisoners.)

pulpit N. raised platform in a church from which sermons are delivered (Stepping to the *pulpit*, the minister began the sermon.)

quake V. to tremble (Her hands shook and she began to *quake* with fear before giving her speech.)

reticent ADJ. quiet and reserved (His *reticent* manner meant that he was often unnoticed in a group.)

stammer V. to speak in a halting manner; repeat letters or words involuntarly (In her excitement, she began to *stammer* and trip over her words.)

Exercise 1
Write the letter of the word that best completes the sentence.

1. Speak clearly and try not to _____ your speech.   _____
   A. impede   B. dictate   C. garble   D. enumerate

2. The preacher stood at the _____ to speak.   _____
   A. pulpit   B. lecturer   C. lisp   D. keynote

3. I will _____ the items we need for the trip.   _____
   A. disparage   B. impede   C. exhort   D. enumerate

4. The wise old man offered _____ to those in need of advice. _____
   A. keynote   B. lisp   C. counsel   D. proclamation

5. The _____ of the rally was providing shelter for the homeless. _____
   A. pulpit   B. counsel   C. keynote   D. lecturer

6. Even though she was difficult to understand, we thought her _____ was charming. _____
   A. pulpit   B. lisp   C. keynote   D. proclamation

7. If you _____ the letter now, it can by typed before you leave. _____
   A. enumerate   B. quake   C. emanate   D. dictate

8. The speaker's powerful _____ moved the audience to tears. _____
   A. oration   B. keynote   C. lecturer   D. pulpit

9. His reply was so _____ that we could not understand it. _____
   A. emanate   B. forceful   C. inarticulate   D. reticent

10. His feelings will be hurt if you _____ his attempts at playing baseball. _____
    A. dictate   B. disparage   C. exhort   D. garble

Exercise 2
Choose the word that most nearly has the *same* meaning as the italicized word.

11. *lecturer*   A. guest   B. speaker   C. listener   D. audience   _____
12. *exhort*   A. sing   B. deny   C. whisper   D. incite   _____
13. *forceful*   A. strong   B. funny   C. weak   D. careless   _____
14. *reticent*   A. noisy   B. angry   C. shy   D. friendly   _____
15. *inane*   A. foolish   B. careful   C. pleasant   D. short   _____
16. *impede*   A. help   B. block   C. walk   D. erase   _____
17. *quake*   A. stand   B. speak   C. follow   D. shake   _____
18. *stammer*   A. pound   B. stutter   C. throw   D. laugh   _____
19. *proclamation*   A. declaration B. compliment   C. secret   D. package   _____
20. *emanate*   A. buy   B. sell   C. return   D. originate   _____

ANSWER KEY

Spelling Development

Spelling Master 1
Pages 1–2

Practice the Words
1. Achieving; achievement
2. confining; confinement
3. severe; severity
4. endorsement; endorsing
5. festive; festivity
6. aging; ageless
7. amuse; amusing
8. defense; defenseless
9. love; lovely
10. timing; time

Apply What You Know
Answers will vary. Possible answers are given.
1. likely; likable
2. completely; completion
3. intensely; intensive
4. pricing; priceless
5. stately; statement
6. financing; financial
7. legislator; legislature
8. engaged; engagement

Proofreading Practice

To avoid purchasing items you will later regret owning, follow these rules. first, never buy impulsivly. Second, research more expensive items to see if they meet your requirments and to see if they can be bought for a more lower price. Don't be impressed by celebrities' endorsements of products. Taking time to be a carful consumer will save you time money, and aggravation in the end.

Spelling Master 2
Pages 3–4

Practice the Words
1. defied
2. Celebrities
3. conveyed
4. centuries
5. employed
6. attorneys
7. applies
8. displays, displaying
9. subways
10. envied

Apply What You Know
1. theories
2. modifying
3. justified
4. medleys
5. controversies
6. tallied
7. dignified
8. decoys

Proofreading Practice

There are a number of controversys over the plan to build a network of subwayes connecting two suburban Countys to the City. The most important issue is whether such a costly project is justifyed. Some independant transportation agencys have suggested a modifyed version of the plan that seems more realistically. The Commission needs to examine all it's alternatives before undertaking such an enormous project.

Spelling Master 3
Pages 5–6

Practice the Words
1. blurred
2. zipper
3. summed
4. fitness
5. sweetly
6. weaken
7. stealing
8. summary
9. madly
10. darken
11. sums
12. weakness

Apply What You Know

1 + 1 + 1 words: beg, gun, throb, thin, stun

Across
3. stunned
6. heiress
7. funniest
8. beggar
9. raining
10. throbbing

Down
1. eaten
2. wooden
4. thinnest
5. shearing

Proofreading Practice

There once was a pauper who fell madly in love with a woman who happened to be the heiress to a large fortune. Each night he spoke to her under the cover of darkness. The woman was charmed by this mysterious visitor and ask^ed him to marry her. At this, the young man disclosed that he was poor. Although stun^ned by his revelation, the woman said "I would rather marry a beggar than a braggart any day" Thus, the two were married and lived happy ever after.

Spelling Master 4
Pages 7–8

Practice the Words
1. editor
2. submitted
3. admittance
4. traveler
5. occurrence
6. crediting
7. benefited
8. inference
9. permitted
10. preference

Apply What You Know

o mit′   con cur′   pro′ fit   re cur′   can′ cel
quar′ rel   of′ fer   in cur′   re mit′   com mit′

1. canceling
2. omitted
3. incurring
4. remittance
5. quarreled
6. recurrence
7. concurrent
8. committed
9. offering
10. profited

Proofreading Practice

If you like exciting movies, then I highly recommend An Occurence at Owl Cave. The movie is about Adam, a time traveller who is transported to a prehistoric age. He is permit^ted to join a primitive clan of cave people, and it is soon evident to he/him and the audience that he will be submit^ted to a number of trials. Somehow adam endures a grate/great deal of suffer^ing. Although the story is admit^tedly a little far-fetched, the acting is very beli^evable. If you enjoy science fiction, then you wo^n't be disappointed by this action-packed adventure.

Spelling Master 5
Pages 9–10

Practice the Words
1. concession
2. persuade
3. proclaim
4. dissuade
5. restrain
6. dissatisfied
7. procession
8. recession
9. incorporate
10. congenial

Apply What You Know
1. edict
2. verdict
3. dictated
4. dictator
5. prediction
6. contradictory
7. rejected
8. dejection
9. objecting
10. projection
11. projectile
12. interjected

Proofreading Practice

Nobody should feel inhibited by using a camera. By following some basic guidelines you can become an exceptional photographer. For instance, watch the way the light reflects off your subject or you will get undesirable shadows. Also, prevent objects, such as your finger from obstructing the lens. Third, try to judge the distance between you and your subject carefully. Or your photograph will be fuzzy. Most importantly, keep persevering. With practice you may eventually take exhibition-quality photographs.

Spelling Master 6
Pages 11–12

Practice the Words
Acceptable hyphenation will vary. In general, most words should be divided according to pronunciation. Possible answers are provided.
1. author-ity (less acceptable: au-thority, authori-ty)
2. victo-rious (less acceptable: vic-torious, victori-ous)
3. his-tory (less acceptable: histo-ry)
4. reg-ular or regu-lar
5. imag-inary or imagi-nary
6. popu-larity or popular-ity (less acceptable: pop-ularity, populari-ty)
7. famil-iar (less acceptable: fa-miliar)
8. ordi-narily or ordinar-ily (less acceptable: or-dinarily, ordinari-ly)
9. tempo-rarily or temporar-ily (less acceptable: tem-porarily, temporari-ly)
10. major-ity (less acceptable: ma-jority, majori-ty)

Apply What You Know
1. pe cu′ liar; pe cu′ li ar′ i ty
2. mem′ o ry; me mo′ ri al
3. mi′ nor; mi nor′ i ty
4. ed′ i tor; ed′ i to ri′ al
5. so′ lar; so lar′ i um
6. reg′ u lar; reg′ u lar′ i ty
7. sec′ re tar′ y; sec re tar′ i al
8. vol′ un tar′ y; vol′ un tar′ i ly
9. su pe′ ri or; su pe′ ri or′ i ty
10. li′ brar y; li brar′ i an

Proofreading Practice

How do you cope with entering a new school? Here are some tips. to make new friends, seek out students with interests that are similar to yours instead of trying to join the popular crowd. One way to do this is to join after-school clubs and activities. Keeping your grades up can be a major problem, so do your homework regularly. Ask your teachers for help if you need it. To avoid getting lost, familiarize yourself with the building before school starts. Create clever memory tricks to help you remember your locker combination. Don't worry. You'll be a pro in no time at all.

Spelling Master 7
Pages 13–14

Practice the Words

The first word in each item below should be circled. The second word is the appropriate spelling word. Possible sentences are provided. The sentences that expand each phrase will vary.

1. uncertain; doubtful; We are doubtful about her ability to handle the assignment.
2. peacefully; calmly; The mother calmly reassured her frightened child.
3. beat; rhythm; I enjoyed the rhythm of the drums.
4. noodles; spaghetti; We cooked the spaghetti and sauce for fifteen minutes.
5. artist; designer; The fashion designer added a new fall line of clothing to her collection.
6. deadened; numbed; My fingers were numbed by the cold temperatures.
7. thinking; psychology; My brother is studying child psychology in college.
8. sentence; condemn; The judge will condemn the criminal to a life of hard labor.

Apply What You Know

1. campaign
2. subtle
3. psalm
4. plumber
5. ghetto
6. autumn
7. rhyme
8. qualm
9. gnaw
10. poignant

Proofreading Practice

I'm indebted to that plummer who soldered my

   broken heart,

and to his gnu who nawed its way through my

   apple tart.

I have no dout that this little tune will some day be

   maligned,

But its got a good rhythm, and it's certainly one of

   a kind.

There are nine words that contain silent letter combinations.

Spelling Master 8
Pages 15–16

Practice the Words

Sentences will vary. Possible answers are given.

1. Yes, the man can prove his <u>innocence</u>.
2. A student must have a C average to be <u>eligible</u>.
3. Yes, the furnishings were very <u>elegant</u>.
4. Billy seems to have a <u>suspicious</u> look on his face.
5. No, often one's impressions are not easily <u>communicable</u>.
6. Yes, I think he was being intentionally <u>ambiguous</u>.
7. The cowboy sought <u>vengeance</u> for the murder of his companion.
8. I think Chicago has the most <u>magnificent</u> skyline.

Apply What You Know

1. negligence
2. extravagance
3. complacent
4. applicant
5. invincible
6. applicable
7. navigable
8. intangible

Proofreading Practice

Dear Friend of Nature,

   The snow leopard is one of the most

magnificent animals on earth. It's heavy, pale-gray

coat keeps it warm and enables it to travel

inconspicuous in the Himalayas. But negligance,

extravagence, and complacancy is bringing this

irreplaceble creature to the verge of extinction.

You see, poachers are killing the snow leopard

for its fur. A coat made from this rare leopard's pelt

will sell for over $30,000. You can help stop the

illegal poaching of animals such as the snow

leopard by sending us your contribution today.

Spelling Master 9
Pages 17–18

Practice the Words
1. crises (P)
2. fungi (P)
3. data (P)
4. radius (S)
5. analysis (S)
6. criteria (P)
7. basis (S)
8. stimuli (P)
9. diagnosis (S)
10. medium (S)

Apply What You Know
The order of the answers may vary.
1. stadium—stadiums
2. vacuum—vacuums
3. agenda—agendas
4. aquarium—aquariums
5. octopus—octopuses
6. appendix—appendixes
7. index—indexes
8. hypnosis—hypnoses
9. axis—axes
10. oasis—oases
11. alumnus—alumni
12. nucleus—nuclei

Proofreading Practice

The general practitioner, or G.P. is often called the family doctor. General practioners care for all kinds of illnesses, from treating simple fungis infections to removing appendexes. To identify an illness, a G.P. usually examine a patient and performs tests. He or she then use the test results and other datas as the basis for his or her diagnoses. A G.P. may treat a patient with drugs, or in a crises, may refer a patient to a specialist.

Spelling Master 10
Pages 19–20

Practice the Words
1. restaurant
2. chauffeur
3. pigeon
4. gourmet
5. surgeon
6. coupon
7. tourist
8. silhouette
9. soldier
10. limousine
11. souvenir
12. lieutenant

Apply What You Know
1. carousel
2. poultry
3. dungeon
4. croutons
5. mousse
6. acoustics
7. camouflage
8. boulevard
9. chandelier
10. rendezvous

Proofreading Practice

Congratulations! You have just winned a weekend in Paris! On Friday at noon, a limosine will take you from the Paris airport to your hotel. At 6:00 P.M. your private chaffeur will take you to Julienne's, a gourmet restaraunt along Boulevard St.-Michel. We recommend you try the roast pigon with cruotons or the cheese soufflé On Saturday and Sunday you can shop for soveniers along the banks of the Seine river or visit the Palace of the Louvre. Show the enclosed copoun in the museum shop to receive a gift. We hope you will enjoy your visit!

Vocabulary Development

Lesson 1 Cuisine
Pages 21–22

Exercise 1
1. C	4. B	7. C	10. B
2. D	5. C	8. A	
3. A	6. D	9. B	

Exercise 2
11. C	14. C	17. B	20. B
12. A	15. D	18. A	
13. C	16. D	19. C	

Lesson 2 Law
Pages 23–24

Exercise 1
1. B	5. B	9. C	13. C
2. A	6. A	10. D	14. B
3. D	7. D	11. A	15. D
4. C	8. B	12. B	

Exercise 2

16. B An *attorney* works in a *courtroom;* a *doctor* works in a *hospital.*
17. C *Inequity* is an antonym of *justice; light* is an antonym of *dark.*
18. D *Unwittingly* is a synonym of *unknowingly; habit* is a synonym of *custom.*
19. B A *jury* has a *juror* as a member; a *team* has a *player* as a member.
20. A *Divorce* is an antonym of *marriage; tall* is an antonym of *short.*

Lesson 3 Money and Finance
Pages 25–26

Exercise 1
1. C	4. A	7. A	10. C
2. A	5. B	8. D	
3. D	6. D	9. B	

Exercise 2
11. C	14. C	17. A	20. B
12. A	15. D	18. C	
13. A	16. C	19. D	

Lesson 4 School Days
Pages 27–28

Exercise 1
1. B	5. A	9. D	13. A
2. A	6. B	10. C	14. B
3. D	7. D	11. D	15. C
4. C	8. C	12. D	

Exercise 2

16. A *Idle* is an antonym of *busy; asleep* is an antonym of *awake.*
17. B *Reprimand* is a synonym of *scold; close* is a synonym of *shut.*
18. B *Intellectual* describes things having to do with the *mind; physical* describes things having to do with the *body.*
19. D You *distribute papers;* you *plant seeds.*
20. A A *provocation* is a cause for *anger;* a *flame* is a cause of *heat.*

Lesson 5 Feelings
Pages 29–30

Exercise 1
1. C	4. D	7. B	10. D
2. A	5. C	8. C	
3. B	6. A	9. B	

Exercise 2
11. B	14. D	17. B	20. D
12. A	15. A	18. A	
13. C	16. C	19. C	

Lesson 6 Editing and Writing
Pages 31–32

Exercise 1
1. C	4. A	7. A	10. C
2. A	5. B	8. B	
3. D	6. D	9. D	

Exercise 2
11. C	14. A	17. A	20. C
12. B	15. A	18. B	
13. D	16. D	19. B	

Lesson 7 Construction
Pages 33–34

Exercise 1

1. D	5. A	9. D	13. D
2. B	6. C	10. A	14. A
3. A	7. D	11. C	15. B
4. D	8. A	12. B	

Exercise 2

16. C You *solder wires* together; you *glue papers* together.
17. A You can *renovate* an old *building;* you can *recycle* old *newspapers.*
18. D *Insulation* keeps a *house* warm; a *coat* keeps a *person* warm.
19. B *Hovel* is a *synonym* of *shack; mistake* is a synonym of *error.*
20. A *Faulty* is the adjective, and *fault* is the noun; *exploding* is the adjective, and *explosion* is the noun.

Lesson 8 Sports
Pages 35–36

Exercise 1

1. B	4. C	7. B	10. D
2. A	5. D	8. C	
3. D	6. B	9. A	

Exercise 2

11. C	14. D	17. D	20. B
12. B	15. B	18. A	
13. A	16. A	19. C	

Lesson 9 Behavior
Pages 37–38

Exercise 1

1. B	5. D	9. B	13. C
2. B	6. A	10. D	14. B
3. A	7. C	11. B	15. D
4. B	8. B	12. C	

Exercise 2

16. A *Congenial* is an antonym of *disagreeable; dirty* is an antonym of *clean.*
17. B *Defy* is a synonym of *rebel; carry* is a synonym of *haul.*
18. B An *extrovert* can be described as *talkative;* a *whistle* can be described as *shrill.*
19. C An *ingrate* can never be *thankful; rain* can never be *dry.*
20. D *Unstable* is a synonym for *temperamental; happy* is a synonym for *glad.*

Lesson 10 Nature and Wildlife
Pages 39–40

Exercise 1

1. B	4. A	7. D	10. C
2. A	5. C	8. A	
3. D	6. C	9. B	

Exercise 2

11. A	14. A	17. C	20. D
12. B	15. A	18. B	
13. D	16. C	19. B	

Lesson 11 Mystery and Suspense
Pages 41–42

Exercise 1

1. B	4. C	7. D	10. B
2. D	5. B	8. C	
3. A	6. A	9. D	

Exercise 2

11. B	14. D	17. B	20. A
12. D	15. C	18. A	
13. A	16. A	19. D	

Lesson 12 Clothing and Fashion
Pages 43–44

Exercise 1

1. C	5. D	9. B	13. D
2. A	6. A	10. C	14. A
3. B	7. B	11. C	15. B
4. A	8. C	12. C	

Exercise 2

16. B You *alter* a *dress* to change it; you *remodel* a *house* to change it.
17. A *Rustle* is the sound of *leaves; chime* is the sound of a *bell.*
18. D A *reduction* will *lower* the price; an *increase* will *raise* the price.
19. B *Informal* is a synonym of *relaxed; smooth* is a synonym of *even.*
20. A *Miscellaneous* is an antonym of *identical; damp* is an antonym of *dry.*

Lesson 13 Travel
Pages 45–46

Exercise 1

1. C	4. D	7. D	10. A
2. B	5. C	8. C	
3. A	6. B	9. B	

Exercise 2

11. B	14. A	17. C	20. C
12. C	15. A	18. D	
13. A	16. D	19. B	

Lesson 14 Government
Pages 47–48
Exercise 1

1. B	4. D	7. C	10. C
2. C	5. A	8. D	
3. B	6. A	9. B	

Exercise 2

11. B	14. D	17. C	20. A
12. A	15. C	18. B	
13. A	16. B	19. D	

Lesson 15 Medicine
Pages 49–50
Exercise 1

1. C	4. B	7. B	10. D
2. A	5. D	8. A	
3. B	6. B	9. B	

Exercise 2

11. C	14. B	17. C	20. D
12. A	15. A	18. B	
13. C	16. D	19. A	

Lesson 16 History
Pages 51–52
Exercise 1

1. C	4. A	7. C	10. C
2. A	5. C	8. B	
3. D	6. B	9. D	

Exercise 2

11. A	14. A	17. D	20. A
12. B	15. B	18. B	
13. C	16. C	19. C	

Lesson 17 Language and Literature
Pages 53–54
Exercise 1

1. D	5. C	9. C	13. B
2. B	6. B	10. B	14. D
3. D	7. C	11. D	15. A
4. B	8. B	12. A	

Exercise 2

16. A *Symbolize* is a synonym of *represent;*
    disappear is a synonym of *vanish.*
17. C *Enrich* is the verb, and *enrichment* is the
    noun; *enjoy* is the verb, and *enjoyment* is the
    noun.
18. C *Unsavory* is an antonym of *honorable;*
    cloudy is an antonym of *clear.*
19. D You *unravel* a *mystery* to find the answer;
    you *solve* a *problem* to find the answer.
20. C *Improper* can describe poor *behavior;*
    unsightly can describe poor *appearance.*

Lesson 18 Transportation
Pages 55–56
Exercise 1

1. D	4. A	7. A	10. B
2. B	5. B	8. C	
3. C	6. D	9. A	

Exercise 2

11. B	14. D	17. B	20. B
12. D	15. B	18. C	
13. A	16. D	19. B	

Lesson 19 Suffixes — -ation/-tion/-ion/-sion
Pages 57–58
Exercise 1

1. C	5. B	9. D	13. A
2. C	6. A	10. B	14. B
3. D	7. D	11. D	15. D
4. B	8. C	12. B	

Exercise 2

16. B *Sanitation* can prevent *disease; caution* can
    prevent *accidents.*
17. A *Deception* is the noun, and *deceive* is the
    verb; *election* is the noun, and *elect* is the verb.
18. C *Perception* is the synonym of *insight; tall* is a
    synonym of *high.*
19. D A *promotion* means a better *job;* a *raise*
    means a better *salary.*
20. A *Deprivation* is an antonym of *prosperity;*
    ancient is an antonym of *modern.*

Lesson 20 Agriculture
Pages 59–60
Exercise 1

1. D	4. D	7. B	10. C
2. A	5. A	8. D	
3. C	6. C	9. B	

Exercise 2

11. C	14. A	17. C	20. A
12. A	15. A	18. A	
13. C	16. B	19. D	

Lesson 21 The Military
Pages 61–62

Exercise 1

1. B	5. A	9. A	13. B
2. D	6. D	10. D	14. D
3. C	7. B	11. B	15. A
4. B	8. C	12. D	

Exercise 2

16. C *Strategic* is the adjective, and *strategy* is the noun; *beautiful* is the adjective, and *beauty* is the noun.
17. C To *barricade* is to *prevent* someone from going through; to *open* is to *allow* someone to go through.
18. A *Civilian* is an antonym of *military; wet* is an antonym of *dry.*
19. B *Sentry* is a kind of *guard; palomino* is a kind of *horse.*
20. C You can show *bravery* in the face of *danger;* you can show *generosity* in the face of *need.*

Lesson 22 Headline News
Pages 63–64

Exercise 1

1. B	5. A	9. D	13. B
2. A	6. D	10. C	14. C
3. C	7. B	11. B	15. D
4. A	8. A	12. C	

Exercise 2

16. B *Controversial* can describe an *issue; funny* can describe a *movie.*
17. D A *drought* is not enough water, and a *flood* is more than enough water; a *famine* is not enough food, and a *feast* is more than enough food.
18. C A *summit* is at the top, and a *base* is at the bottom; *high* is at the top, and *low* is at the bottom.
19. B *Unbiased* is a synonym of *fair; cool* is a synonym of *chilly.*
20. D *Endless* is a synonym of *everlasting; carefree* is a synonym of *lighthearted.*

Lesson 23 Performing Arts
Pages 65–66

Exercise 1

1. C	4. D	7. A	10. A
2. B	5. C	8. D	
3. A	6. B	9. C	

Exercise 2

11. C	14. B	17. D	20. C
12. A	15. D	18. A	
13. C	16. C	19. B	

Lesson 24 The Home
Pages 67–68

Exercise 1

1. B	4. B	7. B	10. C
2. D	5. D	8. A	
3. A	6. C	9. B	

Exercise 2

11. C	14. D	17. B	20. C
12. B	15. A	18. D	
13. A	16. D	19. A	

Lesson 25 Suffixes— *-ful/-ous*
Pages 69–70

Exercise 1

1. B	4. D	7. A	10. A
2. D	5. B	8. C	
3. B	6. C	9. D	

Exercise 2

11. C	14. A	17. D	20. C
12. A	15. B	18. A	
13. D	16. B	19. B	

Lesson 26 Occupations
Pages 71–72

Exercise 1

1. B	5. C	9. B	13. B
2. C	6. B	10. A	14. C
3. D	7. D	11. C	15. A
4. A	8. A	12. B	

Exercise 2

16. C An *aviator* steers an *airplane;* a *driver* steers a *car.*
17. B A *warden* has charge of a *prison;* a *captain* has charge of a *ship.*
18. A An *apprentice* helps you learn a *skill; study* helps you learn a *subject.*
19. C A *mason* works with *stone;* a *painter* works with *paint.*
20. B A *chaplain* works in the field of *religion;* a *doctor* works in the field of *medicine.*

Lesson 27 Actions
Pages 73–74

Exercise 1

1. B	4. D	7. D	10. D
2. D	5. B	8. B	
3. A	6. A	9. A	

Exercise 2

11. B	14. B	17. D	20. A
12. A	15. D	18. B	
13. D	16. A	19. C	

Lesson 28 Health
Pages 75–76

Exercise 1

1. C	4. A	7. D	10. A
2. A	5. D	8. C	
3. B	6. C	9. B	

Exercise 2

11. B	14. A	17. C	20. A
12. A	15. D	18. B	
13. C	16. C	19. D	

Lesson 29 Art and Music
Pages 77–78

Exercise 1

1. C	5. B	9. B	13. D
2. A	6. C	10. D	14. C
3. B	7. D	11. B	15. B
4. A	8. A	12. A	

Exercise 2

16. B *Attentive* is an antonym of *unobserving; hot* is an antonym of *cold.*
17. D *Clarity* is the noun and *clear* is the adjective; *beauty* is the noun and *beautiful* is the adjective.
18. A *Sustain* is a synonym of *hold; happy* is a synonym of *joyful.*
19. A You *replay* a *sonata* to become more familiar with it; you *reread literature* to become more familiar with it.
20. C You *tinge* by adding a small amount of *color;* you *season* by adding a small amount of *salt.*

Lesson 30 Science
Pages 79–80

Exercise 1

1. B	4. A	7. C	10. A
2. D	5. B	8. B	
3. B	6. A	9. C	

Exercise 2

11. A	14. D	17. A	20. C
12. D	15. C	18. D	
13. B	16. A	19. B	

Lesson 31 Hobbies
Pages 81–82

Exercise 1

1. A	4. C	7. D	10. A
2. D	5. B	8. C	
3. B	6. D	9. D	

Exercise 2

11. A	14. A	17. C	20. D
12. C	15. C	18. A	
13. D	16. B	19. C	

Lesson 32 Business
Pages 83–84

Exercise 1

1. A	4. A	7. D	10. D
2. C	5. B	8. C	
3. B	6. B	9. B	

Exercise 2

11. A	14. D	17. C	20. A
12. C	15. B	18. B	
13. A	16. A	19. D	

Lesson 33 Animal Life
Pages 85–86

Exercise 1

1. C	5. B	9. A	13. A
2. A	6. A	10. C	14. D
3. D	7. D	11. D	15. A
4. B	8. C	12. B	

Exercise 2

16. A *Wily* is a synonym of *sly; city* is a synonym of *town.*
17. C A *pelt* covers a *fox; feathers* cover a *duck.*
18. D *Constrict* is an antonym of *expand; friend* is an antonym of *enemy.*
19. A *Lope* is the movement of a *cheetah; hop* is the movement of a *rabbit.*
20. B A *tusk* is a tooth for an *elephant;* a *molar* is a tooth for a *person.*

Lesson 34 Prefixes—*di-/dis-*
Pages 87–88

Exercise 1

1. B	5. B	9. D	13. B
2. D	6. C	10. B	14. A
3. A	7. A	11. B	15. B
4. C	8. D	12. C	

Exercise 2

16. B *Disgorge* is a synonym of *vomit; car* is a synonym of *auto.*
17. A You *disburse money;* you *sew seeds.*
18. C You *disrobe* before a *bath;* you *dress* before a *party.*
19. B *Distract* is the verb, and *distraction* is the noun; *carry* is the verb, and *carrier* is the noun.
20. D *Discord* is an antonym of *harmony; up* is an antonym of *down.*

Lesson 35 Prefixes—
co-/con-/com-
Pages 89–90

Exercise 1

1. B	4. A	7. A	10. A
2. C	5. D	8. B	
3. D	6. C	9. C	

Exercise 2

11. B	14. A	17. A	20. D
12. D	15. C	18. D	
13. B	16. D	19. C	

Lesson 36 Verbal Communication
Pages 91–92

Exercise 1

1. C	4. C	7. D	10. B
2. A	6. C	8. A	
3. D	7. B	9. C	

Exercise 2

11. B	14. C	17. D	20. D
12. D	15. A	18. B	
13. A	16. B	19. A	